PEIRCE'S THEORY
OF SCIENTIFIC DISCOVERY

Peirce Studies
Number 3

Kenneth Laine Ketner, general editor

Institute for Studies in Pragmaticism
Lubbock, Texas

PEIRCE'S THEORY OF SCIENTIFIC DISCOVERY

A System of Logic
Conceived as Semiotic

BY

RICHARD TURSMAN

INDIANA UNIVERSITY PRESS
BLOOMINGTON AND INDIANAPOLIS

Manufactured in the United States of America

Library of Congress Cataloging-in-Publication Data
Tursman, Richard Allen, 1932-
Peirce's theory of scientific discovery.

(Peirce studies; no. 3)
Bibliography: p.
Includes index.
1. Science—Methodology. 2. Science—Philosophy.
3. Semiotics. 4. Peirce, Charles S. (Charles Sanders),
1839–1914. I. Title. II. Series.
Q175.T825 1987   501   85-45764
ISBN 0-253-34295-3

1   2   3   4   5   91   90   89   88   87

To Marie

CONTENTS

PREFACE

Charles Sanders Peirce was born in Cambridge, Massachusetts, on September 10, 1839. From 1861 to 1891 he worked as a geodesist for the United States Coast and Geodetic Survey. In 1887 he and his wife, Juliette, moved to Milford, Pennsylvania, and the following year they purchased 130 acres of land just north of Milford on the Delaware river. On this land they constructed a very large house which Peirce called *Arisbe*. In 1947 the Pennsylvania Historical and Museum Commission placed just outside the Peirce house an historical marker which reads:

CHARLES S. PEIRCE
The noted philosopher, logician, scientist and founder of pragmatism lived in this house from 1887 until his death in 1914. America's most original philosopher and greatest logician, a great part of his work was written here.

One important theme running throughout the writings of Peirce scholars is that Peirce was working out a philosophical *system*. In his 1923 *Chance, Love and Logic*, for example, Morris Cohen referred to Peirce's vast philosophical system and indicated that Peirce left only some fragmentary outlines of this system.[1] The 1952 *Studies in the Philosophy of Charles Sanders Peirce* opened with a letter from Professor Lovejoy suggesting that the Peirce Society undertake to bring Peirce's whole scheme of ideas into a clearer focus than Peirce himself had done, that this scheme of ideas had certainly been conceived by Peirce to be a system, and that after bringing this system into clearer focus the Society should submit it to a methodological and searching criticism.[2]

In Feibleman's 1960 work Peirce's philosophy was interpreted as a system;[3] in Murphey's 1961 work Peirce's philosophy was described as a sequence of systems;[4] in Apel's work of the 1960s and 70s Peirce's philosophy was portrayed as developing in a unified way and in an architectonic way from Kant's philosophy;[5] in Herbenick's 1970 article it was suggested that Peirce was the silent precursor of the *systems era*;[6] and in his 1980 work Esposito expressed the opinion that while Peirce had generally been regarded as a philosopher either with several systems or with two basic philosophical concerns (epistemology and metaphysics), he was working out a unified interdisciplinary and scientific metaphysical system.[7] Among those who have been studying Peirce's system, there have been certain points of agreement: for example, it has been generally agreed that his system is based upon the three categories (Weiss expressed this opinion in his 1940 article, "The Essence of Peirce's System"[8]); that his system is essentially an objective idealism resembling Schelling's; and that his system is scientific, objective and open—Feibleman said it was *hodogetic*, whatever that means.[9]

While there has been an interest in Peirce's system and some agreement about its fundamental features, a number of philosophers have been less than enthusiastic about it. Buchler, in his 1940 criticism of Weiss's article, argued that while Peirce did intend a system, it was not clear that it was based upon the three categories or that pragmatism was any sort of system, though synechism was itself a systematic regulative principle.[10] Russell, in his foreword to Feibleman's book, said that most modern readers would find Peirce's system unduly metaphysical and too much influenced by evolutionary optimism; Russell then suggested that even when Peirce's general system is discarded, there remain many fruitful suggestions in his philosophy.[11] In 1954 in criticizing earlier Peircean scholarship, Lieb wrote, "They try to see his *tangled skein of contradictions* and his *outcroppings here and there* as an organic unity. Yet their presentations most often have constructive shortcomings; for they do not tell us well enough what an organic unity is, nor do they show us well enough how the contradictions and outcroppings find their place in a systematic order."[12] And Mora, in a 1955 article, after agreeing that Peirce was undoubtedly haunted by the idea of a system, made the good point that what kind of system it was remained to be seen.[13]

In my opinion Peirce had very little respect for philosophical systems of the traditional type and he never attempted to work out such a system. He did, however, have a great deal of respect for logic and he did attempt to work out a system of logic. While he never completed this system, he left sufficient information concerning it for us to make out at least its fundamental structure. It is a system of logic in a very wide sense of the term *logic,* as the reader will easily see. At times Peirce equated logic in this wide sense with semiotic or the theory of signs. Peirce was very well acquainted with the reasonings of mathematicians and other scientists and he was most interested in the anatomy of scientific discovery. Before Peirce, no attempt to delineate the anatomy of scientific discovery along purely logical lines had been successful. The gap between the dynamic and complex world of scientific discovery, on the one hand, and the severely limited categories of traditional logic, on the other hand, was too great for traditional logic to bridge. Peirce developed a new, revolutionary kind of logic, powerful enough to narrow the gap between logic and the world of scientific discovery. Peirce regarded every step in science as a lesson in logic and after many long and difficult lessons, the observant logician learns what logic must be in order to be powerful enough to encompass the domain of scientific discovery. It is no accident that Peirce's system of logic is, at the same time, a theory of scientific discovery, for it was designed to be just that.

PEIRCE'S THEORY
OF SCIENTIFIC DISCOVERY

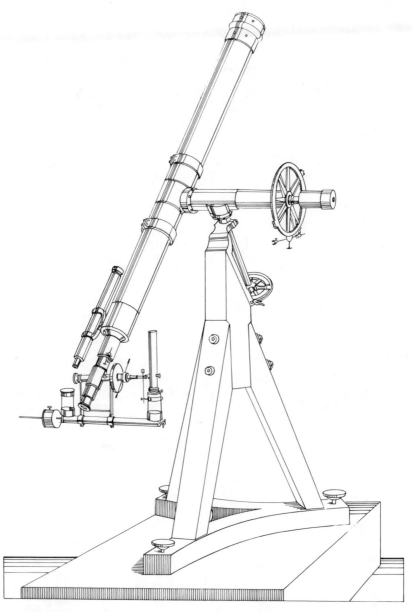

A Zöllner astrophotometer shown connected to a six-foot refractor of the Leipzig observatory. The lithograph is by J. G. Bach from a photograph by S. H. Vogel and occurs as Plate VI in Johann C. F. Zöllner's *Photometrische Untersuchungen:* Leipzig, 1865.

INTRODUCTION

Peirce was both a philosopher and a scientist and from this vantage point he gained some new and interesting insights into the nature of these disciplines and the relationships between them.

Of the multitude of philosophers (including logicians) who influenced the development of Peirce's thought, those who influenced it most were probably Kant, Boole, and Whewell. Peirce began his study of Kant in 1855 and for a decade remained essentially a Kantian.[1] In 1863 Peirce referred to Kant's *Critic of Pure Reason* as "the greatest work of the human intellect. All later philosophies are to be classified according to the ideas contained in it."[2] ("Critic" was Peirce's preferred translation; he believed "Critique" to be a mistranslation.) Of course Peirce admired the entire Copernican revolution in philosophy; he shared Kant's contempt for dogmatism; he admired Kant's attack on positivism. But what Peirce admired most about Kant, that single Kantian point of greatest importance to Peirce, was Kant's conception of logic as the "science of the laws of the mind's action or what is the same thing of [sic] the forms of thought in general."[3] Kant had argued that the categories of cognition were isomorphic with the categories of traditional logic. Peirce believed the categories of cognition were isomorphic with the categories not of traditional logic but of exact logic.

The foundations of exact logic had been laid by George Boole. In 1865 Peirce wrote:

> Perhaps the most extraordinary view of logic which has ever been developed with success is that of the late professor Boole of Dublin. His book is entitled *An Investigation of the Laws of Thought, on Which Are Founded the Mathematical Theories of Logic and Probabilities*. It is destined to mark a great epoch in logic: for it contains a conception which in point of fruitfulness will rival that of Aristotle's *Organon*.[4]

1

In a series of papers he wrote in the 1870s and 80s, Peirce improved and extended Boolean algebra to the point where it became Peirce's own exact logic, the logic of relations (or what Peirce called the logic of relatives). The first paper in this series had the title, "Description of a Notation for the Logic of Relatives, Resulting from an Amplification of Boole's Calculus of Logic."[5] In this paper was put forward the leading idea of the new exact logic, namely, to take the *illative* relation (the illative relation resembles the *implication* relation) as the fundamental relation in logic instead of any other relation, such as the *identity* relation as Boole had done. As Peirce developed his exact logic through this series of papers, it came to include other new and significant ideas, such as that of triadic and higher order relations, that of quantifiers and indices, and that of a system of relations (or a system as that which is defined in terms of relations).[6] It is pointed out in a recent article by Hilary Putnam that while Peirce did not invent the quantifier, he was the first to develop its use and it was through Peirce that quantification worked its way into modern mathematical logic.[7] Peirce used the logic of relations in a number of ways of mathematical interest, such as to express fundamental relations involving probabilities[8] and to express linear algebra in terms of matrices.[9] A development of Peirce's logic of relations as a calculus can be found in Schröder's *Vorlesungen über die Algebra der Logik (Exakte Logik)*.[10] The Boole-Peirce-Schröder school was the leading school of mathematical logic at the end of the nineteenth century and the notation this school introduced remained in use for some time.[11]

In Peirce's view the importance of exact logic lay not in the direction of the development of mathematics or mathematical logic (such as demonstrations or theorems), but in the direction of a development of a general logic of the sciences.[12] He believed (as one aspect of developing a general logic of the sciences) that exact logic had a most important role to play in our search for the categories of thought. Peirce's investigations of the categories proceeded concurrently with his researches in exact logic; he continuously revised his doctrine in both domains; and he constantly had an eye out for isomorphisms between the two domains by virtue of which he could unify them into one system of logic.

In later years, as Peirce moved away from the transcendental idealism of Kant, the system of logic he developed resembled in a few very general respects the idealisms of Schelling, Hegel, and Royce.[13] Every ideal-

ism sought the categories of thought and no idealism was exempt from
the duty of determining these categories as accurately as possible. Something of the spirit of Peirce's notion that the search for the categories
should be in conjunction with exact logic can be picked up by contrasting
his attitude toward Hegel (on the one hand) with his attitude toward
Royce (on the other hand). After 1890 Peirce was saying that he no
longer held Hegel in contempt and that his own philosophy resuscitated
Hegel—though in a strange costume.[14] With Hegel, Peirce appreciated
the scope of the observation that what we have before us is the intellect's
description of what passes before it, as opposed to having before us, say,
original or first impressions of sensation;[15] and Peirce agreed that "Hegel was quite right in holding that it was the business of this science
[phenomenology] to bring out and make clear the Categories or fundamental modes."[16] But what Peirce always found objectionable about Hegel was that Hegel's method of finding the categories had "the defect of
not working at all if you think with too great exactitude."[17] Hegel's
procedure yielded arbitrary solutions as opposed to determinate solutions and, Peirce announced, he did not find a single step in Hegel's
logic convincing or persuasive.[18] With a different idealist, Royce, Peirce
had more in common: both were constructing a comparative morphol-
ogy of concepts;[19] both admired Kempe's "Theory of Mathematical
Form;"[20] both sought to modify an Hegelian type philosophy in whatever way the results of science recommended;[21] and both admired
Peirce's logic of relations. Royce wrote:

> There has gradually come into being a reformed logic,—a logic still very
> imperfectly expounded in even the best modern textbooks, and as yet
> hardly grasped, in its unity . . . but a logic which is rapidly progressing,
> which is full of beauty, and which is destined, I believe, profoundly to
> influence, in the near future, our whole philosophy of truth.[22]

Royce never followed up this poetry by indicating how the new logic
would influence our philosophy of truth, except to try to identify analogues of basic relations in the social, political, and religious realm. For
example, in a work called, "The Hope of the Great Community," Royce
argued that all genuine communities were triadic and were "communities of interpretation."[23] If the reader is interested in this line of development of Peirce's logic, he will find something of it in Apel's notion of
a *Kommunicationsgemeinschaft.*[24]

Whewell published *The History of the Inductive Sciences* in 1837 and *The*

Philosophy of the Inductive Sciences in 1840.[25] In 1893, looking back, Peirce wrote that his own studies in the history of science had on the whole confirmed Whewell's view that progress in science depended upon "the observation of the right facts by minds *furnished with appropriate ideas*."[26] Of course Whewell was a Kantian but this did not impress Peirce so much as did the fact that Whewell constructed a theory of science based upon an exhaustive study of the history of all natural sciences.[27]

It is unfortunate that while several twentieth-century schools of philosophy have picked up an idea or two of Peirce's along the way, none has picked up a Peircean idea within the context of Peirce's system of logic. For example, the school of Carnap, Reichenbach, Kneale, von Wright, and others, tried to work out an inductive logic, and in this attempt gave serious consideration to Peirce's ideas that probabilities depended on relative frequencies and that inductive inferences were self-corrective, but not to either of these ideas within the context of Peirce's system of logic.[28]

In some remote respects a first step toward seeing Peirce's ideas within the context of his system of logic was taken with the publication in 1949 of H. Butterfield's *The Origin of Modern Science*.[29] It was Butterfield's thesis that no problem was more central to the scientific revolution than the problem of understanding *motion* and that the revolution itself was essentially an adopting of new ways of looking at motion. While it was fashionable in Butterfield's time to think of the scientific revolution as having been brought about by the discovery of new facts, by experimentation, and by the application of some sort of logic (deductive or inductive), he maintained that it was not such factors which stood at the heart of the scientific revolution, but rather the circumstance that Galileo and others looked at old facts in new ways. For example, Galileo was now seeing natural motion *as* inertial motion rather than as motion requiring a constant contact force to sustain itself. It was T. Kuhn's *The Structure of Scientific Revolutions*[30] which, more than any other work, developed Butterfield's thesis (in terms of *paradigm shifts*) and brought philosophers of science around to paying more attention to the history of science as they proceeded to develop their logics of science.

In the second half of this century there has been a general shift of interest away from the "context of justification" of ideas or theories and toward the "context of discovery." In contemporary philosophy of science, the most interesting question is whether or not there is a logic of hypothesis generation. Putting it in other words, the most interesting problem is, "What is the anatomy of discovery?"

In the spring of 1973, the Smithsonian, the National Academy of Sciences, and the Copernicus Society of America held a great festival in Washington, D.C., honoring the 500th anniversary of the birth of Copernicus. The theme of the festival was "The Nature of Scientific Discovery."[31] On the second day of the festival Gerald Holton presented a paper with the title, "Mainsprings of Scientific Discovery." After mentioning the current mood of scepticism concerning the methods of science and the current controversy concerning the place of science in national and intellectual life, Holton made the following suggestion:

> At the very least, we have to ask ourselves what the conditions may be that conduce to the strengthening or weakening of science. I shall steer away from questions of funding, or manpower, or the politics of science, and other worthy issues that have been debated often enough. I want to concentrate instead on the precious center of scientific work, the nature of the process of scientific discovery.[32]

Holton next pointed out that in the past scientists had been reluctant to describe how they hit upon their discoveries, and philosophers of science, until recently, had not directed their attention to the context of discovery, the result of such attitudes being "to discourage the study of this 'jungle.' "[33] Holton suggested that things were getting better in that many scientists now report to historians, psychologists, and sociologists what goes on in the creative phase of their discoveries. Finally, Holton went on to sketch his own view of this creative phase which he saw as based upon "thematic presuppositions."

Volume 56 of *Boston Studies in the Philosophy of Science* has the title *Scientific Discovery, Logic and Rationality;* its companion volume, volume 60, has the title *Scientific Discovery: Case Studies;* these volumes were published in 1980.[34] In his introduction to these volumes Thomas Nickles says that they open "a new period in philosophy of science, one in which discovery, innovation, and problem solving will take their places as a legitimate area of study;"[35] and, Nickles says, he counts himself among the "friends of discovery."[36] Since Peirce's system of logic or theory of scientific discovery addresses itself to many of the same issues as those which interest the friends of discovery, Peirce's system of logic in this respect fits nicely with contemporary philosophy of science.

While Peirce's thought has elements in common with nineteenth and twentieth century philosophy, including logic, including current interest in the history of science and in scientific discovery, it would be more accurate to view his system of logic or theory of scientific discovery not as a philosophical theory but as a scientific theory within the tradition of Newtonian natural philosophy. Peirce was very much in favor of a great cooperative effort in which those of us (philosophers?) whose business it was to observe the most general would do so, and those of us (scientists?) whose business it was to observe the less general would do so. Peirce drew a polar distinction between *cenoscopy* and *idioscopy:* the cenoscopic sciences are based upon observations of more general things such as general ideas or the general features common to any given perception (phenomenology, for example, is a cenoscopic science if its observations are not inexact and subjective as are Husserl's);[37] the idioscopic sciences are based upon observations of more particular things such as the position of a spectral line, and typically require special equipment such as a spectroscope (crystallography, for example, is an idioscopic science). Theoretically, as any given idioscopic science went along, it would report from time to time *its results,* having made *its* observations and done *its* reasoning. And as any given cenoscopic science went along, it would report *its results.* The science of esthetics, for example, would let the community know approximately what was of value in itself; the science of ethics would let us know approximately what we ought to do (what controls would be necessary) in order to achieve our goals; the science of metaphysics would let us know what space, time, matter, and motion were. The difficulty Peirce encountered when he turned to the philosophers for their *results* was that they (with the exception of logicians) had no results to report.

In 1974 a symposium was held (at a meeting of the History of Science Society) on the topic, "Charles Sanders Peirce: Scientist, Mathematician, and Historian of Science."[38] At that symposium, after giving reasons for believing Peirce to be our greatest American philosopher, Max Fisch made the following remark:

> But it was not until the early 1950s midway in the Society's first half-century, that Carolyn Eisele began her long series of articles on Peirce as historian of science, as scientist, and as mathematician. It was not until the 1960s that Victor Lenzen began the series of articles in which he has

brought the competence of a physicist to the closer analysis and evaluation of several ranges of Peirce's scientific work. And it was not until the 1970s that Thomas Cadwallader began trying the hypothesis that Peirce was, among many other things, America's first modern experimental psychologist.[39]

Fisch went on to say that Peirce learned about methods of science by studying the history of those methods, by using those methods himself, and by at the same time contributing to the improvement of those methods. It might be added that Peirce always had his eye open for those methods which had been most *successful* in their own fields and it was these which he looked to most often for help in his research for a general method of discovery. Peirce worked within a dozen or so traditions or scientific communities and it would be difficult to name one he did not learn something from as regards methods of research or as regards important ideas. Here, I shall mention only two such traditions. I have selected those two which I think were the most useful to Peirce and the most influential in the development of his theory of scientific discovery.

After the publication of Newton's *The Mathematical Principles of Natural Philosophy* (1687), two great traditions developed within the history of astronomy: mathematicians such as Euler, D'Alembert, Lagrange, and Laplace developed the mathematical principles of celestial mechanics; and then there were the "great observers" such as Herschel (who constructed huge reflecting telescopes, discovered Uranus, and made observations of the brightness and distribution of stars and nebulae in an effort to find out the structure of the heavens) and Bessel (who first observed stellar parallax and first worked out a theory of "reducing" observations).

Laplace's *Celestial Mechanics*[40] (which was completed in 1825) contained equations for predicting the motions of the moon, the motions of the planets, the motions of the entire solar system! According to Bowditch (see below), the object of Laplace's book was to reduce all the known phenomena of the system of the world to the law of gravity.[41] A remarkable feature of these equations is that they formed a system with a few at the top (stated in terms of generalized co-ordinates and generalized forces) from which less general equations followed. The mathematical methods developed in celestial mechanics were so general that they were applicable to any mechanical system. One can take, say, a pulley system, note its degrees of freedom, initial state, and a few other factors, and then derive an equation which predicts the motion of this pulley system from one of the very general equations of mechanics such as "the general Lagrangian." Nathaniel Bowditch translated Laplace's *Celestial Mechanics* into English and was aided in this task by Benjamin Peirce, Charles Peirce's father. In 1855, when Benjamin Peirce completed his own *Analytic Mechanics*,[42] he dedicated it to his "master in science," Nathaniel Bowditch.[43] Benjamin Peirce, who had a tremendous influence on his son, Charles, was most impressed with the fact that so much about the real physical world could be deduced from these most general equations. Benjamin Peirce wrote that the worthy occupation of an immortal soul was to work with these formulas organized into theory which penetrated the whole domain of physical science.[44] Benjamin Peirce would often write the equation $\sum P \, \delta\rho = 0$[45] on the blackboard, step back, admire it, and remind his students that this equation was the universal type by which every problem of mechanics was subjected to analytic discussion.[46] In 1872 Charles Peirce was placed in charge of gravity determinations for the U.S. Coast Survey. These determinations were made with a mechanical system, namely with a compound pendulum (of one variety or another). During the mid 1870s Charles Peirce made an extensive study of analytic mechanics and, with the help of his father, became quite proficient at setting up and solving the differential equations needed to relate his measurements to the general laws of mechanics. Victor Lenzen's opinion was that it was by virtue of *this* facility of Peirce's (more than anything else) that Peirce was one of the leading physicists of his time.[47]

In nineteenth-century America the "great observers" included Ogden Rood ("father of American experimental physics"), author of *Modern Chromatics;*[48] Henry A. Rowland, who designed new diffraction gratings and mapped the solar spectrum; and Albert Michelson, who developed the interferometer and performed, in collaboration with Edward Morley, the famous experiment which proved there was no ether drift. In an article in which he was describing the virtues of his new diffraction gratings, Rowland wrote:

> Another important property of the concave grating is that all the super-imposed spectra are in focus at the same point, and so by micrometric measurements the relative wave-lengths are readily determined. Hence, knowing the absolute wave-length of one line, the whole spectrum can be measured. Professor Peirce has determined the absolute wave-length of one line with great care and I am now measuring the coincidences.

> This method is greatly more accurate than any hitherto known, as by a
> mere eye inspection, the relative wave-length can often be judged to 1
> part in 20,000 and with a micrometer to 1 in 1,000,000.[49]

In connection with his work in spectroscopy, metrology, and geodesy,
Peirce was frequently making hundreds of careful *observations*. Those
which were most immediately relevant to his theory of scientific discovery were those he made in astrophotometry. In his first book, *Photometric Researches* (1878),[50] Peirce reported measurements of stellar magnitudes he had made with the use of an instrument called a Zöllner
astrophotometer.[51] The purpose of this research was to increase the
number of stars available as standards for navigational and astronomical purposes, to improve the estimates of stellar magnitudes listed in
previous star catalogs, to determine which stars were variable, and to
draw whatever inferences could be drawn from this data concerning
the distribution of stars in space and the shape of our galaxy. The basic
operation of the Zöllner astrophotometer was as follows: light from a
petroleum lamp was thrown on one side of the optical field and light
from a star on the other; these two lights (which were phenomenal
lights) were then matched in brightness by varying the intensity of the
light from the lamp which was gradually polarized with a rotating Nicol
prism system. Peirce found that the brightness of the phenomenal light
from the lamp varied in intensity as a logarithmic function of the
measured intensity as read off the degree of rotation of the prism
system (in accord with Fechner's psycho-physical law). This is an interesting case for phenomenology because the reading on the instrument
is an index of the strength of phenomenal light, not to be confused
with the strength of the incoming light waves which was relatively
"noumenal." Peirce used this instrument also to observe the colors of
stars and to study variations in color with variations in brightness. He
found that as brightness increased, hues shifted toward the red end of
the spectrum. Peirce considered photometric observations to be of
great value in Phenomenological research, because here, in the world
of hues and brightnesses and saturations, one encountered "a multitude of sensations as unaltered by the operation of the intellect, and as
near to the first impressions of sense, as any perception which it is in
our power to extricate from the complexus of consciousness . . . ."[52] As
a member of the community of scientists, Peirce looked upon his theory of scientific discovery (his system of logic) as a theory put forward

on the basis of *results* he had obtained concerning the logical features of scientific inquiry—*results* not different in kind from those he had obtained in spectroscopy, geodesy, or photometry, other than in being more cenoscopic and less idioscopic.

While Peirce began his study of chemistry when he was eight years old and wrote a history of chemistry when he was eleven, his study of logic did not begin until the ripe old age of twelve with his reading of Whately's *Elements of Logic*. As the years went by, Peirce eventually studied the writings of almost every ancient, medieval, and modern logician, including, for example, the writings of Aristotle, Scotus, Leibniz, DeMorgan and Lange. In 1882, after having studied logic for more than thirty years, Peirce wrote:

> "*Dyalectica*," says the logical text-book of the middle ages, "*est ars artium et scientia scientiarum, ad omnium aliarum scientiarum methodorum principia viam habens* [Dialectic is the art of arts and the science of sciences, possessing the way to the principles of the methods of all the other sciences]," and although the logic of our day must naturally be utterly different from that of the Plantagenet epoch, yet this general conception that it is the *art of devising methods of research,*—the *method of methods,*—is the true and worthy idea of the science.[53]
>
> This is the age of methods; and the university which is to be the exponent of the living condition of the human mind, must be the university of methods.[54]
>
> And it must be confessed that we students of the science of modern methods are as yet but a voice crying in the wilderness, and saying prepare ye the way for this lord of the sciences which is to come.[55]

In 1885, Peirce expressed the opinion that what he was in the world for was to "set forth the true nature of logic, and of scientific methods of thought and discovery."[56] And later, in 1902, he wrote: "Although the number of works upon Methodeutic since Bacon's *Novum Organum* has been large, none has been greatly illuminative. . . . THE book on this subject remains to be written: and what I am chiefly concerned to do is to make the writing of it more possible."[57]

Peirce planned and completed portions of a treatise on scientific discovery. The title he proposed for this treatise was: "*Reason's Conscience: A Practical Treatise on the Theory of Discovery Wherein Logic Is Conceived as Semiotic.*"[58] In a letter to William James (December 25, 1909),[59] Peirce indicated that his system of logic was to regard logic as the theory of signs in general and that his system would consist of three books. A *sign* is, roughly, anything whatsoever—real objects, imaginary objects, abstract relations, physical properties, concepts, facts, laws, etc.—as it is thought of. I shall delay defining a *sign* until chapter 3. Peirce defined *semiotic* as a cenoscopic science of signs and as a trivium of formal sciences of symbols in general.[60] The first department is called *speculative grammar:* it is a study of the general conditions of signs being signs,[61] a study of what kinds of signs are absolutely essential to the embodiment of thought,[62] a classification of different possible signs,[63] and a study of the essential nature and fundamental varieties of possible semiosis.[64] The second department is called *critical logic:* it is a study of the formal conditions of the truth of signs,[65] of the general conditions of the reference of signs to their objects,[66] and a classification of arguments and a determination of the validity and degree of force of each kind.[67] The third department is called *speculative rhetoric:* it is a study of sign-action in the world as manifested, for example, by unseen molecular forces[68] and a study of the essential conditions under which a sign may determine an interpretant or bring about a physical result.[69]

While Peirce thought of his system of logic as semiotic, he thought of it also as a modal logic. During the Arisbe period (1887–1914), Peirce was developing further his exact logic (the logic of relations) along the lines of modal logic, with attention centered around the three modalities—possibility, actuality, and probability.[70] In the *Minute Logic* of 1902, Peirce introduced an alternative set of names for the three departments of his system of logic: the first department, the department concerned primarily with possibility, he called *originalian logic;* the second department, concerned primarily with actualities, he called *obsistent logic;* and the third department, concerned primarily with probabilities, he called *transuasional logic.*[71]

When Peirce's system of logic is conceived as semiotic, the best names for the three departments are *speculative grammar, critical logic,* and *speculative rhetoric:* I shall refer to these as the *semiotic names.* When his system of logic is thought of as essentially a modal logic, the best names for the three departments are *originalian logic, obsistent logic,* and *transuasional logic:* I shall refer to these as the *modal names.* A disadvantage of the modal names is that Peirce did not use them after 1902 (whereas he did use the semiotic names). A disadvantage of the semiotic names is that Peirce was not *sure* it was a good idea to conceive his system as semiotic[72] (if not, the best alternative would be to conceive it as a modal logic). In what follows I shall use the modal names and the semiotic names more or less interchangeably.

The immediate purpose of Peirce's system of logic is to make science intelligible in the same sense that a rule which generates a number sequence or a deductive system or a theory of differential equations makes its particular domain intelligible. Intelligibility is achieved upon the occasion that everything in a given domain may be seen clearly to be the offspring of or a subcase of a minimal number of the most general kinds of relations or ideas.[73] In an effort to achieve this purpose, Peirce classified and ordered (1) the kinds of ideas it is possible for any inquirer to have; (2) the kinds of inferences it is possible for any inquirer to draw; and (3) the kinds of laws nature is likely to obey. And he settled for no classifications or orderings of any domain which were not parts of a single classification and ordering of the entire field of science. While the immediate concern of Peirce's system is with the purely logical aspects of scientific discovery,[74] the system has the practical or economic value of maximizing the likelihood that the concepts, methods, and results of one science might actually be used by another or related to those of another.[75]

A last point which might be made, by way of introduction, is that in Peirce's opinion physics could advance no further without logic. Physics had advanced in the past because it had been able to observe its objects directly; this was no longer possible in the case of atomic physics. Peirce was particularly interested in the question of whether or not there were atomic forces different in kind from central forces between pairs of particles; in 1896 he wrote, "It is not too much to say that this question is the principal question to-day in natural philosophy."[76] He believed that as the new generation of physicists moved ahead to explore the world of light, electricity, magnetism, molecules, atoms, and other parts of what in Peirce's day was called the "unseen universe," they would of course want to form hypotheses concerning this universe; the problem, however, was that they had no experience of it and therefore no basis of information upon which to form their hypotheses. The solution Peirce proposed to this problem was, in effect, that physicists could observe the atomic realm indirectly by observing thought and could in that way have at least some foundation for their hypotheses. It was this circumstance, his belief that physicists needed to observe the forms of thought, which led Peirce to say that physicists stood in special need of logic.[77]

I

SPECULATIVE GRAMMAR (1)

Norwood Hanson is given credit for having challenged the once popular view that there was a logic of justification of hypotheses but not a logic of discovery. In his *Patterns of Discovery* (1958), Hanson revived Peirce's notion that there is a mode of reasoning called "hypothesis" or "retroduction" or "abduction" and Hanson described this form of inference as:

>(Premiss 1)   Some surprising phenomenon *P* is observed.
>(Premiss 2)   *P* would be explicable as a matter of course if
>   *H* were true.
>
>(Conclusion) There is reason to think *H* is true.[1]

This is accurate in the sense that in 1903 Peirce gave the form as:

>(Premiss 1)   The surprising fact, *C*, is observed.
>(Premiss 2)   But if *A* were true, *C* would be a matter of course.
>
>(Conclusion) There is reason to suspect that *A* is true.[2]

Hanson and others[3] are quick to point out that this form of inference does not itself purport to be the form of inference to an hypothesis as a new idea, for *H* is obviously contained in the premisses. Rather than inferring *H* from *P*, we are inferring that *H* might be true on the grounds that *P* would be a matter of course, given *H*. But if the core of retroduction is that *H* implies *P* then its core is the same as the core of the Hypothetico-Deductive method, so that these two modes of reasoning are not essentially different. Peirce himself emphasized that *the* reason for thinking *H* might be true is that *H* would explain *P*.[4]

There is a tendency in contemporary philosophy of science to divide the logic of discovery into three logics: (1) the logic of the generation of new ideas or hypotheses; (2) the logic of pursuit and/or of preliminary evaluation of hypotheses; and (3) the logic of the justification of hypotheses. (These three logics do not correspond to the three departments of Peirce's system of logic.) Peirce is usually credited with having contributed to the logic of the justification of hypotheses by virtue of his extensive work on inductive procedures. Peirce is credited also with having contributed to the logic of pursuit by virtue of his work on the regulative principles of abduction. (Regulative principles are characteristics desirable in hypotheses such as depth or explanatory power, consistency with established bodies of knowledge, simplicity, meaningfulness, and amenability to testing. Peirce usually discussed such *desirabilia* under the topic of the *economy of research*. For an account of Peirce's philosophy of science which focuses its attention upon the economy of research in this and closely related senses, the reader is referred to Nicolas Rescher's *Peirce's Philosophy of Science: Critical Studies in His Theory of Induction and Scientific Method.*[5]) The view has been expressed by Curd that abduction was really intended by Peirce to be a logic of pursuit, primarily, and that in order to bring out this point, the logical form of abduction given above should be modified to read:

(Premiss 1)   The surprising fact, *C*, is observed.
(Premiss 2)   The hypothesis, *A*, is capable of explaining *C*.

(Conclusion) There are *prima facie* grounds for pursuing *A*.[6]

Supporting Curd's view is Peirce's statement that an abduction concludes that such and such an hypothesis may be true and "that the indications of its being so are sufficient to warrant further examination."[7] Peirce is not usually credited with having contributed to the logic of the generation of new ideas or hypotheses, but he should be because he did contribute to this logic as well as to the other two logics. It is true that Peirce never described any logical step-by-step process of generating new ideas; and it may be true, as Martin Curd says, that in fact Peirce "rejected the idea of an algorithm for generating theories."[8] As the first of the three departments of his system of logic, however, Peirce outlined an originalian logic which addresses itself to the question of how new ideas or hypotheses arise in the mind and of what kinds these may be.

Peirce wrote, in his Harvard lectures of 1865, "There is a large class of reasonings which are neither deductive nor inductive."[9] This large class of reasonings always consistently remained in Peirce's mind as that one of the three classes of reasonings which introduced new ideas or hypotheses into science. In 1865, to pick an early date, he referred to the third mode of reasoning as "reasoning to a physical hypothesis."[10] And in 1901, to select a late date, he referred to the third mode as reasoning which took its start in facts and sought a theory.[11]

That there may be three fundamental modes of reasoning was suggested to Peirce by (among other things) the circumstances that the valid syllogisms may be reduced to three basic forms. By conversion the valid syllogisms we are familiar with today can be reduced to these six forms:

First Figure: All A is W.
(Barbara,   All or Some S is A.
Darii)
                 All or Some S is W.

Third Figure: All or Some S is not W.
(Festino,   All or Some S is A.
Bocardo)
                 Some A is not W.

Second Figure: All S is W.
(Camestres,   All or Some A is not W.
Baroco)
                 All or Some A is not S.

Peirce experimented with the *nota notae* forms of these deductions, with forms of them involving marks and ratios of marks, with forms of them involving samples and populations and ratios of each, and with other "statistical syllogisms." He introduced the interesting Rule, Case, Result interchanges which relate third and second figure forms to the first figure or "explaining syllogism" form. The suggestion that there may be three fundamental modes of reasoning is brought to the fore and made most prominent when the following kind of analogues of the first, third, and second figures are considered:

First Figure: 2/3 of $A = W$
                 This sample $=$ from A
                 2/3 of this sample $= W$

Third Figure: This sample $=$ from A
                 2/3 of this sample $= W$
                 2/3 of $A = W$

Second Figure: 2/3 of this sample = W
                  2/3 of A = W
                  ──────────────────────
                  This sample = from A

Suppose we have a room with five barrels of apples in it. And suppose
barrel #1 contains 100 red apples, barrel #2 contains 25 red apples
and 75 yellow apples, barrel #3, 50 red apples and 50 yellow apples,
barrel #4, 75 red apples and 25 yellow apples, and barrel #5, 100
yellow apples. Now if we know all this and if we take a random sample
from barrel #3, we expect this sample to be half red and half yellow (or
at least we expect this to be the average of a large number of samples):
this inference is an analogue of the first figure syllogistic inference, and
Peirce called this mode deduction. If we do not know the distribution
of red and yellow apples in barrel #3 but are given a random sample
from barrel #3 and find this sample to contain half red apples and half
yellow apples, we conclude that barrel #3 contains half red and half
yellow apples: this inference seems to be the inverse of the other, is an
analogue of the third figure syllogistic inference, and Peirce called it
induction. If we are shown a sample of half red and half yellow apples
and not told that it comes from barrel #3 but do know the proportion
of red apples and yellow apples in each of the five barrels, we infer that
this sample comes from barrel #3. This is an analogue of second figure
syllogisms and Peirce called this mode of inference hypothesis, retroduction, abduction, and presumption.

The conclusion of the retroduction is that *this* sample comes from *this*
population (barrel #3). The ground of the retroduction is that the
marks of this sample *resemble* the marks of barrel #3 more than the
marks of any of the other barrels and therefore the conclusion to be
drawn is that this sample comes from barrel #3 (most likely). In the
early 1860s and for two decades thereafter, Peirce viewed a retroduc-
tive inference as an inference to the effect that such and such an
hypothesis was likely because there was an observed resemblance between the marks of the sample (or the thing before us to be explained)
and the marks of the hypothesis. Since some resemblances were qualitative and some quantitative, he distinguished between qualitative and
quantitative retroductions. At times he was inclined to think of qualitative retroductions as the basic type and to portray quantitative retroductions as limiting cases of qualitative retroductions. The case (above),
where the marks of the sample are half red and half yellow and re-

semble the marks of barrel #3 exactly and in a quantitative way, is, obviously, a quantitative retroduction. Suppose the sample were 7 red apples and 3 yellow apples: this would be a quantitative retroduction in which the marks of the sample resembled the marks of barrel #4 not exactly, but more than they resembled the marks of any other barrel, so the conclusion would be that *this* sample (of 7 and 3) came from barrel #4. An example of a quantitative retroduction which occurs in Peirce's scientific writings is the following: he concluded that in cross-section our galaxy was a Cassinian oval because the distribution of stars (in a cross-section of our galaxy) resembles the distribution of points which constitute a Cassinian oval.[12] Qualitative retroductions are such inferences as the following: suppose a chemist observes that the liquid in the beaker before him has a pungent odor, feels slippery, burns the skin, and heats up when combined with water. These marks resemble those of some strong acid or base and if the chemist knows that the liquid, whatever it is, is one of the kinds of liquids he keeps in stock, there would be no more than a dozen or so possible hypotheses involved and the chemist could quickly identify the liquid in the beaker.

The main difficulty with these examples of qualitative and quantitative retroductions is that they are in principle supposed to be examples of inferences to hypotheses, but are really inferences to whichever of a number of possible hypotheses already given is best. So in each case what is being investigated is which of a number of initially given sets of marks most closely resembles another initially given set of marks. Peirce described various decision procedures for determining degrees of resemblance between sets of marks, but upon reflection he came to the conclusion that none of these was sufficiently different from induction to warrant a class of its own. So he suggested that all the retroductions or purported retroductions be thrown in with inductions (what Peirce said was that all of the forms of reasoning considered in his Johns Hopkins essay of 1883, which included retroductions, he now, in 1906, classed as inductions).[13] At some point between 1883 and 1906 a transition occurred from an earlier inaccurate view to a later, relatively accurate view of the nature of inferences to new ideas. This transition might conveniently be referred to as a transition from the viewpoint of retroduction or abduction to the viewpoint of originalian logic, if it were not for the circumstance that Peirce continued to call inferences to new ideas retroductions or abductions. For example, in 1903 he wrote, "Abduction must cover all the operations by which theories and conceptions are engendered."[14] But the logic of the emergence of a new idea was, as Peirce called it, an "originary" problem and the terms retroduction or abduction were unsuitable for this logic (see the quotation below concerning remarkable inferences).[15] The substantial logical change in his position was simply that Peirce for the first time brought his attention to focus upon the logic of the emergence of a new idea.

That a really new idea can arise in the mind at all Peirce found *remarkable:* he considered it the Hominidae family's version of natural instinct.[16] He believed our minds were naturally adapted for imagining correct theories and that our natural ideas resembled those of nature.[17] In 1906 he wrote that abduction was no more than guessing, adding that it was a faculty attributed to Yankees.[18] In 1911 he wrote, "I do not, at present, feel quite convinced that any logical form can be assigned that will cover all 'Retroductions.' For what I mean be a Retroduction is simply a *conjecture* which arises in the mind."[19] In his 1954 Ph.D. thesis, John Huggett says that while Peirce searched for a method, what he came up with was empty of all content, amounting to no more than the proposal that inquiry should rely on instinct;[20] and Curd says that the best Peirce could suggest was that there might be a peculiar affinity of the human mind with nature which leads us to guess correctly after only a small number of attempts.[21] There is some truth in what Huggett and Curd say, but, on the other hand, what Peirce contributed to the logic of inferences to new ideas was not that scant.

In 1906 Peirce said that the three most remarkable guesses he knew were: (1) Bacon's guess that heat was a mode of motion; (2) Young's (or Wallaston's?) guess that the primary colors were violet, green, and red; and (3) Dalton's guess that there were chemical atoms. And he said that these guesses were remarkable because they were "most apparently unfounded."[22] In 1911 he returned to the Dalton example, saying,

> However one of the most marvellous and unmistakable cases of what I call (quite unsuitably according to my present views) Retroduction seems to me clearly to have had neither the Quantitative nor the Qualitative form of Abduction. Namely, when Dalton discovered (as he supposed for the first time) that the chemical elements combine in the simplest of multiple proportions, he was seized with such an intense conviction that they were composed of atoms that he never thereafter for a moment doubted it; and stranger still, to my mind, other chemists when they heard of Dalton's theory at once accepted it with hardly more of doubt than Dalton himself entertained.[23]

From the point of view of originalian logic, such an inference, a remarkable inference to a new scientific idea or hypothesis, takes place, typically, in a neighborhood conducive to its emergence. The building of such a neighborhood involves historical, institutional, biographical, and educational factors, but most importantly it must include the presence of appropriate ideas. It is understood, should a new idea emerge, that as regards its truth it will have no greater strength than a conjecture.[24] The new idea will, typically, carry with it a certain force or compulsion; that is, the discoverer will be inclined to "surrender" to its insistence.[25] As originalian logic understands it, the *rationale* for building such a neighborhood and anticipating its product is that no new truth is reached in the absence of such a neighborhood and some new truths are so reached.[26] While it is never known beforehand which ideas will turn out to be appropriate, the likelihood of having an appropriate set at hand is increased, *ceteris paribus,* by collecting and colligating ideas from as many different sciences as possible.

A good share of the attention of originalian logic is focused upon the colligation of ideas. Peirce defined *colligation* as "the binding together of facts by means of a general description or hypothesis which applies to them all."[27] He credited Whewell (the mineralogist) with having been the first to point out to logicians the importance of colligation.[28] Whewell distinguished between the colligation of facts and the explication of conceptions and in his account emphasized the historical aspects of explication and colligation. Originalian logic does not draw this distinction between facts and concepts and in its account emphasizes the logical aspects of colligation. Colligations occur in preparation for the main discovery and at the point of the main discovery. Corresponding to its polar distinction between idioscopic and cenoscopic sciences, originalian logic draws a polar distinction between idioscopic and cenoscopic colligations; and in addition there are mathematical colligations. The following examples are oversimplified, but they will suffice to show the reader what is meant by idioscopic, cenoscopic, and mathematical colligations.

*Example #*1. In studying botany, I observe a great variety of patterns in nature. I classify and order these patterns into a number of types—this is an idioscopic colligation. I find, to take one instance, that the stalks of celery, the thorns of the hawthorn tree, the florets of the pinecone and the sunflower, all fall into helical patterns which are represented by phyllotactic numbers such as 2/3, 5/8, 8/13, and 21/34.[29] In studying mathematics, I find a type of arithmetical sequence called a Fibonacci sequence in which each term is the sum of the two previous terms. For instance, the sequence 1, 1, 2, 3, 5, 8, 13, 21, 34 is such a sequence. This is a mathematical colligation. If these two colligations are brought together in the same neighborhood, the new idea emerges that the numerators and denominators of the pyllotactic numbers are limited to the numbers which comprise the Fibonacci sequence. The observation of this identity is a cenoscopic colligation under the relation of identity.

Example #2. In 1596 Kepler published *The Secret of the Universe.*[30] Even though Kepler left us an account of this discovery, it is not possible to reconstruct a logical account of the process of discovery. But in whatever way the course of events proceeded, at some point the following colligations must have been involved. There are five interplanetary spaces or regions between the portions of the sky occupied by Mercury, Venus, Earth, Mars, Jupiter and Saturn. If the sphere which marks the outer limit of the region occupied by Mercury is considered to have a radius of 1, then the radius of the sphere which marks the inner limit of Venus is 1.4. If the sphere which marks the outer limit of the region occupied by Venus is considered to have a radius of 1, then the radius of the sphere which marks the inner limit of Earth's region is 1.3. Continuing in this way, the value of the outer radii relative to the inner radii of the interplanetary spaces are: between Mercury and Venus, 1.4; between Venus and Earth, 1.3; between Earth and Mars, 1.3; between Mars and Jupiter, 2.8; and between Jupiter and Saturn, 1.5. This is a colligation in the idioscopic science of astronomy. From a study of the last books of Euclid's *Elements,* it is observed that a sphere may be inscribed within each of the five Platonic solids and another sphere circumscribed. The inner sphere touches the faces; the outer sphere touches the vertices. If the radius of the inscribed sphere of the octahedron is taken to be 1, then the radius of the circumscribed sphere is 1.4. If the radius of the inscribed sphere of the icosahedron is taken to be 1, then the radius of the circumscribed sphere is 1.3. Continuing is this way, the relative value of the circumscribed spheres to the inscribed spheres is: for the octahedron, 1.4; for the icosahedron 1.3; for the dodecahedron 1.3; for the tetrahedron 2.8, and for the cube 1.5. This is a colligation in solid geometry. If these two colligations exist in the same neighborhood and it is observed that the sequences are identical, this is a cenoscopic colligation under the relation of identity.

Example #3. Returning to Dalton, his atomic hypothesis was that each kind of matter is composed of small, indivisible particles of the same size, shape, and weight, particles which retain their identity throughout chemical reactions, and particles whose relative atomic weights are, theoretically, determinable. Dalton's attention was turned toward weighing kinds of matter because he was trying to solve various "meteorological" problems such as why air did not stratify and why some gases were more soluble in water than others. The important chemical colligation in the neighborhood was that upon the occasion of two different kinds of matter combining the amounts by weight of each is a simple multiple proportion of the other. For instance, Dalton found that, say, 10 grams of hydrogen combine with 70 grams of oxygen and that 10 grams of magnesium combine with 20 grams of sulphate, so that the simple proportions are 1:7 and 1:2, respectively. Dalton's new idea was to suppose that these simple multiple proportions represented the relative numbers of each kind of matter in a compound atom and hence the relative atomic weights of each kind of matter. This new idea did not come from the data concerning combining weights nor does the idea imply the data. As Peirce put it, "the existence of atoms no more account for the simple ratios of multiple proportions than the fact that a bag of coffee consists of separate 'beans' goes toward proving that if two kinds of coffee are mixed in a bag it must be in some simple proportion."[31] But if the neighborhood includes both this idioscopic chemical colligation (the law of multiple proportions) and the cenoscopic colligation that a whole may be thought of as a sum of unit parts, the final colligation might be made, using the relation of inclusion, that the chemical case before us is such a case.

Originalian logic takes a certain general perspective of scientific discovery: no account of this general perspective can be essentially correct unless it begins with reference to a system of ideas. The first really originalian observation is that as the colligations in a neighborhood reach completion, as they culminate in the emergence of a new idea, the entire set of ideas involved forms part of a system of ideas. This system shows a change of state upon the occasion of a discovery being made. This change of state is defined in terms of ideas (or sets of ideas) which are more determinate or less determinate. To say that one idea (B) is more determinate than another idea (A) (or that one set of ideas is more determinate than another set), is to say that B is more informative than A, or that B represents an increase in information. For example, the idea (B) of a blue star in the constellation Orion contains more information than the idea (A) of some star near the equator. The change from *a star (near the equator)* to *a blue star* and to *a star in the constellation Orion* represents an increase in what Peirce called *informed depth*.[32] The change from knowing (in the case of idea A) that thousands of stars are being designated to knowing (in the case of idea B) that one of the seven brightest stars comprising Orion is being designated (and whichever of these is blue) represents an increase in what Peirce called *informed breadth*.[33] The final colligation is that the star being designated is Rigel, unless Orion contains blue stars other than Rigel.

Colligation is, roughly, the bringing of ideas of a given level of determination under the ideas of a more abstract, more general level of determination. Peirce's system describes which ideas are of widest abstractness or generality or scope and which kinds of further determinations are possible.

Peirce wrote, "the valuable truth is not the detached one, but the one that goes toward enlarging the system of what is already known."[34] The emergence of a new idea is never either a quantum leap to a state of affairs totally unrelated to a previous state of affairs or a continuous transition from one state to another. Both factors are always involved in discovery (and, in fact, in all cases of cognition): as we shall see, Peirce gives more weight to continuity than to abruptness.

In order to describe what originalian logic proceeds to do next, it is necessary first to introduce a very important distinction which Peirce picked up in physics and applied to logic.

There is probably no distinction of greater significance to speculative grammar or originalian logic than the distinction between *process-descriptive* laws and *systems-limiting* laws. To give an account of the early cell-division and subsequent transformations in the development of, say, the pig embryo, is to describe a *process*. To state that the velocity of light does not exceed 2.99×10^8 meters/second or that light moves from air through glass and out again into the air in such a way as to *minimize* its time of travel, is to state *limitations* placed upon the system of nature. A curve may be viewed as a thing generated by a moving point or as a thing built up from points, that is, as a thing built up from the circumstance that a point may be understood as having occupied a number of different positions which may be calculated as a function of the independent variable. This sort of approach to understanding the line, or this account of the genesis of a line, is *process-descriptive*. If, on the other hand, we use the "curve fitting" or "curve tracing" techniques of zeroing in on the position the curve would occupy by calculating the limits within which it lies by taking derivatives to give *maxima* and *minima*, by calculating *x*-axis and *y*-axis intercepts, etc., this is a *systems-limiting* approach. In Lagrangian dynamics or in, say, Benjamin Peirce's *Analytic Mechanics*, the predictions as to how a system of particles is expected to behave are zeroed in on by considering the general degrees of freedom remaining open to a system given whatever limitations are placed upon it. The reader can easily pick up a notion of what the system-limiting approach is by considering the thoughts of an aggressive wrestler. Eyeing his opponent, the wrestler thinks, "Now that I've got him in the corner he can't get out; if he stands up too straight, I'll get a leg takedown; if he leans too far forward, I'll push his head into the mat; if he reaches out quickly with one arm, I'll got for an arm drag." Kepler employed this method in what he referred to as his *war on Mars*. The known positions of Mars were insufficient to reveal its path. By supposing that the sun in some mysterious way *limited* the movement of the planet to a plane and forced the planet to sweep out equal areas of some figure in equal times, Kepler was able to determine that that figure was an ellipse. Reminding one of the *Timaeus* and of the *limits* set upon the plans of the demiurge by Necessity, Kepler wrote:

> There is therefore a conflict between the carrying power of the sun and the impotence or material sluggishness (inertia) of the planet; each enjoys some measure of victory, for the former moves the planet from its position and the latter frees the planet's body to some extent from the bonds in which it is thus held . . . but only to be captured again by another portion of this rotatory virtue.[35]

In their *Elements of Natural Philosophy*, Thomson and Tait explained that so-called "abstract dynamics" was really a species of abstraction which amounted, in effect, to calculating results regarding dynamic systems by limiting the data, "The limitations introduced being themselves deduced from experience, and being therefore Nature's own solution."[36] The motion of a system of particles such as an iron bar, for example, is treated as if the bar were a perfectly rigid body in which case its motion can be described in terms of the translational motion of its center of mass and rotational motion around its center of mass. The law of large numbers may be seen as setting restrictions or limitations upon the kinds of results which will be obtained upon the occasion of our continuing to sample a large population, for these results will fall within certain limits as we zero in on the population mean.[37]

Given this distinction between process-descriptive laws and system-limiting laws, and given its general perspective that all thoughts form a system of ideas, originalian logic proceeds to investigate the field of cenoscopic ideas in search of all those very general ideas which could be included in any future neighborhood conducive to discovery. The way in which originalian logic carries out this investigation is most interesting: it considers the field of general ideas to have certain constraints upon it, and it is by virtue of these constraints or systems-limiting laws that the domain of general ideas falls into an ordered system of natural classes of general ideas or relations.

II

SPECULATIVE GRAMMAR (2)

In this chapter and in the next, I shall be giving an account of some of the results Peirce obtained when he investigated the field of ideas. He was trying to find out what kinds of ideas were possible and what ideas (if any) were *most* general. Peirce's results suggest that general ideas are ordered; in that respect his results resemble those of group theory which suggest that mathematical ideas are ordered. In this chapter the results I report are stated in the language of what Peirce called *phaneroscopy* or *phanerochemy;* in the next chapter the results I report are stated in the language of what Peirce called *semiotic.* In some respects the two sets of results described in the two chapters are the same results stated in different languages. In some respects the two sets of results are different but complementary.

As was mentioned in the introduction, the development of Peirce's thought was very much influenced by Kant's *Critic of Pure Reason.* Kant's categories represented necessary conditions of judgments about the phenomenal world. It was Kant's view that upon the occasion of our predicating something of a subject, this predication must be determinate in regard to quantity (universal or particular or singular), quality (affirmative or negative or limitive), relation (categorical or hypothetical or disjunctive), and modality (possible or assertoric or apodictic). For example, the judgment that *All Yankees might make good guesses* is universal, affirmative, categorical, and possible. Supposing the *S is P* forms are the fundamental forms of judgments, there remains to be taken into account the fact that paradigmatic instances of knowledge are instances in which we judge that such and such is the case concerning the external world. Kant takes this into account by emphasizing that judgment must be a unity of concept and intuition of an object in (our pure intuitions of) space and time. Upon the occasion that some object appears in the phenomenal field, that is, when we have an intuition of

some object at a particular time and place, we go on to make a judgment about this object and here the unity of thing and concept is a
conditio sine qua non of empirical judgment. This unity of the judgment
as understood by us amounts to just a cross-hair more than the unity
simpliciter, and is referred to by Kant as the unity of apperception.
Kant's categories are isomorphic with the forms of judgment of classical logic. As we shall see, Peirce had three categories and these are
isomorphic with the forms of his new logic of relations. Peirce retained
in his system Kant's category of relation and he retained Kant's two
modal categories of possibility and necessity (provided necessity be
taken in a sense closer to actuality or existence than to logical necessity).
Peirce dropped Kant's category of apodictic certainty or *must be* because
he believed inferences were never known to be infallible. He reduced
Kant's category of quantity to relations (with the help of quantifiers
and indices). The *is non* of the category of *quality* Peirce saw as no
different in meaning from *is not* which became the negation relation.[1]
The *is* of identity became the identity relation. The *is* of equivalence
became a bi-conditional. The other senses of *is* all became relations of
some kind in Peirce's system, the most interesting case being the *is* of a
synthetic judgment such as *this stove is black.* Kant's view was that in such
a judgment the intuition (this stove) is combined with the concept
(black), the result of which is a synthetic unity of understanding.
Peirce's view was that what is understood is that this embodied black
here in this stove is related to the concept black by being a further
determination of the concept black. In 1894 Peirce said that his category of thirdness (which we shall describe shortly) was predominant in
the synthetic unity of consciousness.[2]

In his investigation of ideas, Peirce intended to examine all possible
kinds of ideas and toward this end the first thing it was pertinent to
examine was "the most universal categories of elements of all experience, natural or poetical."[3] What Peirce examined in order to discover
the most universal categories of experience was what he called the
phaneron, the study of which he called *phaneroscopy* or *phanerochemy.* As a
chemistry of the mind phanerochemy examines the *elements* and *compounds* of thought. It does not take these to be material elements and
compounds, but it does take them to resemble material elements and
compounds in important respects. We shall say what a *phaneron* is
shortly. Before doing so, the point might be made that the first result
Peirce got in phanerochemy was that there are *three* most general ideas

or categories or elements of thought. He called these *thirdness, second-ness,* and *firstness,* and he warned his readers that these ideas were "so excessively general . . . that . . . they must seem . . . vague."[4] And, he added, these were three ideas "lying upon the beach of the mysterious ocean. They are worth taking home, and polishing up, and seeing what they are good for."[5]

Phanerons are intervals of thought ranging in duration from a few hundredths of a second up to a life-time. The fastest pass by altogether too quickly to be examined at the time, directly. Peirce gave the example of how he could estimate the end-point of a swing of the seconds pendulum to within a tenth of a millimeter even though the pendulum is within that interval for no longer than a twentieth of a second.[6] Phanerons include everything, of course, all feelings, memories, hopes, desires, the present, all cognitions, all we might "conjure up."[7] Concerning phanerons Peirce wrote:

> There is nothing quite so directly open to observation as phanerons; and since I shall have no need of referring to any but those which (or the like of which) are perfectly familiar to everybody, every reader can control the accuracy of what I am going to say about them. Indeed, he must actually repeat my observations and experiments for himself, or else I shall more utterly fail to convey my meaning than if I were to discourse of effects of chromatic decoration to a man congenitally blind. What I term *phaneroscopy* is that study which, supported by the direct observation of phanerons and generalizing its observation, signalizes several very broad classes of phanerons: describes the features of each; shows that although they are so inextricably mixed together that no one can be isolated, yet it is manifest that their characters are quite disparate; then proves, beyond question, that a certain very short list comprises all of these broadest categories of phanerons there are; and finally proceeds to the laborious and difficult task of enumerating the principal subdivisions of those categories.[8]

In phanerochemistry we try to zero in on the elements of thought by making a "sketch of ourselves,"[9] that is, we attempt to zero in on the general features of thought just as in curve-tracing we attempt to zero in on the general form of a curve. What Peirce observed, and what all other phanerochemists would observe (presumably), is that phanerons are continuous, monotonic, and open.[10] They are continuous in the sense that they have no breaks in them and no parts; they are monotonic in the sense that there is a mediation from the first to a last part as thought streams from past to future; and they are open in the sense that they have no discrete beginning or ending. A most interesting feature of phanerons is that these same properties obtain no matter how long or how short the phaneron under examination may be.

Any random phaneron, including a *shortest phaneron,* meets the conditions that it is continuous, monotonic, and open. In "Questions Concerning Certain Faculties Claimed for Man," Peirce argued that we do not in fact observe isolated, discrete thoughts, thoughts unrelated to (thoughts not connected with) other thoughts.[11] What we do observe is that *each phaneron, including* most notably *a shortest phaneron, is itself a miniature continuum;* the "parts" of ideas are *welded* together: a second succeeds a first without a gap; a second does not succeed a first like a second tree of a row of trees succeeds the tree before it, in which sort of succession there is a gap between each tree and its successor.[12] What we do not observe are discrete atoms of thought such as Hume's *impressions* or *minimum divisibles* or Mach's *sensations* or Pearson's *immediate sense impressions.* It was Peirce's view that those who believed in such things had not really observed them and were "basing" their belief on *desultory* experience.[13] Further, Peirce wrote that "*observation* as distinct from mere *gazing* consists in perception in the light of a question" and takes considerable practice and skill.[14] If there were any such elements of thought, Peirce believed, we were not conscious of them.[15]

Suppose we focus our attention upon the *shortest phaneron* we possibly can. An interesting question concerning a *shortest phaneron* is this: what are the *minimum* number of factors involved in it? This problem is similar to the following problem: what is the *minimum* number of colors which will suffice to color the countries shown in any given map in such a way that no adjacent countries are colored the same? (It has been suggested but not proved that the answer to this problem is four.) In the case of the phanerochemical problem, Peirce observed that a *minimum* of three factors is involved in a shortest phaneron: namely, the idea of one thing combined in a continuous way to another.[16] Whether this connection is relatively objective as in a fusion of two pieces of metal or as in the crystallization of a salt out of a concentrated solution, or relatively subjective as in an *understanding* that one thing is connected with another, there are always, at any point along this gradient, *three* inextricably continuous *factors* and, accordingly, Peirce calls this most general feature of phanerons *thirdness.* Thirdness is prominent in the mathematical idea of a generating operation, in the ideas of growth, diffusion, development, regularity, and law.[17] Thirdness is the most indeterminate limitation upon thought, the most general *conditio sine qua non* of consciousness, that is, of ideas. The idea of *thirdness* is approximately the same as the idea of continuity and approximately the same as the idea of *synechism*.

Secondness is difficult to define, but upon the occasions where mediation or combination reaches a minimum, there are abrupt contrasts and determinate things which at that point seem to force themselves upon us.[18] For example, the external world appears as something other than the internal world; the quality red appears as something other than the quality blue; a possibility appears as something other than a necessity. Suppose a vector $\vec{R}$ is the resultant of the vectors $\vec{A}$ and $\vec{B}$. $\vec{R}$ could have been the resultant of any number of pairs of vectors, but $\vec{R}$ is the resultant of just precisely $\vec{A}$ and $\vec{B}$ and not of any other pair; that *this* pair is the pair of which $\vec{R}$ is the resultant, here and now, is a *second*. Seconds may be a value or have a value, such as this measured value of c or g. We have no idea why seconds have the values they do have; it is just that the universe *is* one way rather than another, that is, such and such seconds simply are in the system.[19] Seconds are seconds by virtue of having forced themselves into experience. A second is an *haecceity,* a this-here-now feature of the phaneron which is an indication to us of existence, quite apart from the question of what exists. Peirce spoke of physical particles, for example, as blindly forcing places for themselves in the world or as willfully crowding their way in.[20] His analogy resembles the wedging analogy Darwin used to describe how individuals struggle to make a place for themselves in the tangled bank of living things.[21] There are degrees of secondness: a dreamlike state has less secondness than a waking state; the number one has less secondness than one existing physical object; the $\sqrt{-1}$ has less secondness than the number 1 or the number -1.[22] Peirce gave the following example of a second: "Let the Universe be an evolution of Pure Reason if you will. Yet if, while you are walking in the street reflecting upon how everything is the pure distillate of Reason, a man carrying a heavy pole suddenly pokes you in the small of the back, you may think there is something in the Universe that Pure Reason fails to account for."[23]

Firsts are whatever they are independently of a second or a third. They are self-contained and idiosyncratic.[24] They are "positive internal characters" of things.[25] We come across firsts frequently in phanerons due to the circumstance that firsts are the qualities of the things we imagine and perceive, qualities as they are in themselves, not as, say, related to anything else or, say, as embodied in some material object. When I perceive a red apple and my thought dwells on the *red,* this is a first. Another type of first is not a quality as perceived or imagined in itself, but a quality thought of as a potentiality or possibility, as when I consider the *concept red.* The idea of firstness is prominent, Peirce said, in the ideas of feeling, freshness, life, freedom, variety, and spontaneity.[26]

To say that thirdness, secondness, and firstness are the three most general features of thought is not the same thing as to claim that three *pure* phanerochemical elements are given in thought or are observable. What Peirce sometimes says is that a given category is *prominent* in a given idea.[27] Thoughts come along in richly variegated patterns set upon a stage of continuity; we notice ideas clustering in regular patterns and we notice a mix of irregularity and regularity in these patterns; our intuitive notion of time is inseparable from the monotonic feature of the general flow of thought; inseparable from observations of shorter and shorter intervals of time (including, of course, measured intervals); and inseparable from the circumstance that we have a vague, intuitive notion of a present moment of time. All three categories are present in any idea and that in a surprising number of respects. But it was Peirce's view that, the Dionysian nature of thought notwithstanding, the categories were *disparate* (essentially not alike): what might be said is that either thirdness, secondness, or firstness is *predominant* in an idea and the idea may be classified accordingly.

In some respects an idea becomes what it is in the course of being observed. And in some respects how an idea is classified is a function of *how* it is observed, of the ways which the idea *can be* related to other ideas and *is* so related. In order to do justice to such complexities, Peirce suggested that ideas be classified in the same way that chemical elements were classified. Nearly a century passed between the time Lavoisier and others identified a number of chemical elements and Mendeleyev successfully classified these into groups by focusing his attention upon the valencies or forms of connection of each element. Peirce wrote that it is "strikingly true that distinctions and classifications founded upon form are, with very rare exceptions, more important to the scientific comprehension of the behavior of things than distinctions and classifications founded upon matter."[28] The elements of ordinary chemistry are classified by *valencies.* Valencies are determined by observing how each chemical element combines with other elements.

Peirce classified phanerochemical elements by observing how they combined with other phanerochemical elements, thus determining their valencies.[29] *A priori*, it would seem that phanerochemical elements could have valencies ranging from zero to indefinitely large numbers. An idea with a valency of zero would be an idea entirely unrelated to any other idea. Such limiting cases (monads or medads) do not appear in the phaneron.[30] Ideas close to these limiting cases do appear in the phaneron. Peirce described such an idea (an element of the phaneron to be assigned a valency of one) as follows:

> Imagine me to wake and in a slumberous condition to have a vague, unobjectified, still less unsubjectified, sense of redness, or of salt taste, or of an ache, or of grief or joy, or of a prolonged musical note. That would be, as nearly as possible, a purely monadic state of feeling. Now in order to convert that psychological or logical conception into a metaphysical one, we must think of a metaphysical monad as a pure nature, or quality, in itself without parts or features, and without embodiment. Such is a pure monad. The meanings of names of "secondary" qualities are as good approximations to examples of monads as can be given.[31]

Every extant quality as experienced or state of consciousness which approximates a monad fails to be a monad; the relation of such ideas to others is minimal; such ideas combine with others with the weakest of bonds; they have a valency of *one*. These firsts or *priman* are relatively complete in themselves but are "capable of composition."[32]

Those ideas which become what they are by virtue of a relation to or dependence on a second idea have a valency of two and are called seconds and, also, *secundan*.[33] Such is the idea of externality. And what is what it is by virtue of a *combination* between two things has a valency of three, called thirds and, also, *tertian*.[34] Once a phanerochemical element with a valency of three is admitted into the system, Peirce believed the essentials of a generating operation were present, so that no *indecomposable elements* with higher than three valencies were necessary or possible. He wrote:

> It is *a priori* impossible that there should be an indecomposable element which is what it is relatively to a second, a third, and a fourth. The obvious reason is that that which combines two will by repetition combine any number. (Thus stated, the principle does not seem to extend to abnumerable multitudes. Yet it must extend to them because, after all, the abnumerable is defined by means of combinations of two, and in-

deed must be so, since there is no form of combination not reducible to that.) *Nothing could be simpler; nothing in philosophy is more important.*[35] [emphasis mine]

(When describing his existential graphs, Peirce wrote, "Now I call your attention to a remarkable theorem. Every polyad higher than a triad can be analyzed into triads, though not every triad can be analyzed into dyads." He illustrated the principle, but it is not clear that he proved the general theorem.)[36] The reason the notion that there is no element with a valency higher than three is so important in philosophy, and nothing else more important, is that if Peirce is right, every other idea or potential category is classifiable by virtue of the way in which it becomes what it is, so that no idea other than thirdness can be the most indeterminate idea involved in its genesis, and with further determinations of thirds we can have a *system* of categories, a system of which categories, such as Kant's, form segments.[37]

If phanerochemical elements are designated (in accord with their valencies) as 3 or 2 or 1, a possible chemical compound could be designated by a juxtaposition of these numbers, forming series such as 12 or 133 or 3121, etc. Such series could represent all the combinations and permutations of phanerochemical elements which would be possible, *a priori*, and it is also possible to think of examples of such series. For example, if the series is given *a priori* as 123, I could think of a *color* and then a *sudden impact* and then the *transition* from my thought of the *color* to my thought of the *sudden impact*. But this is of no interest in phanerochemistry except as a way of getting started on the road to discovering *ordered* series or sequences of elements which have the order they do by virtue of certain necessities or limitations upon the field of thought. Such *ordered* series are *phanerochemical compounds* and represent how a given phanerochemical element *can be* a further determination of a more abstract element. It has been mentioned that in ordinary chemistry valencies are discovered by observing how elements form compounds. The simplest cases are to consider how one element combines with one other element, for example, to consider how calcium combines with chlorine or how carbon combines with oxygen. Peirce examined how one phanerochemical element combined with or related to another and he discovered a method of *ordering* any given pair of phanerochemical elements. These ordered pairings were ordered by degree of generality, so that by recursively applying the method to ideas he was able to order the entire field of ideas. He called his method *prescission*. This method enabled him to reinforce his view that thirdness, secondness, and firstness were the most general ideas, to order these three, to derive secondary and tertiary orders from the highest order of ideas, etc. Hilary Putnam recently pointed out that the expression "first order logic" was due to Peirce.[38] It is at this point in his system of logic, here at the beginning of phanerochemistry, that Peirce begins establishing *orders,* and this by *ordering,* and this by establishing an *ordering operation* or *method of ordering* phanerochemical elements, namely *prescission*.

Prescission is defined as "the act of supposing (whether with consciousness of fiction or not) something about one element of a percept, upon which the thought dwells, without paying any regard to other elements."[39] Prescission is the act of prescinding, which is a special kind of observation the result of which is the ordering of two correlates.[40] Two ideas, A and B, may be either (1) so closely related or associated that we cannot imagine or suppose one without the other, as, for example, larger and smaller; or (2) sufficiently unrelated or unassociated that we can imagine or suppose A without B or B without A, as, for example, red and blue; or (3) related or associated in such a way that we can imagine or suppose A, say, without B, but not the other way around, as, for example, having *a* color (A) without having *this* color (B). If A can be prescinded from BC and B can be prescinded from C, then the result is that B represents a further determination of A and C a further determination of B. For example, since being (something predicated of something) can be prescinded from some subject or object being such and such, and since being such and such can be prescinded from being colored, and since being black can be prescinded from being *this* black, we have an ordered series or sequence or system of ideas.

When A can be prescinded from B, B is then the result of a further determination of A. A is *abstract* relative to B and B is *concrete* relative to A. B has a "more primary mode of substantiality"[41] than A. If, for example, A is a filament, this filament is abstract relative to B where B is a particle which resulted from a further determination of the filament. Peirce liked to say that the reality of the more abstract consists in the truth regarding the less abstract, that is, the reality of the being of the filament consists in the being of something else, the particle.[42] After a mathematician shows in a very clear way that one thing, B, does result from a further determination of a second thing, A, he can then see very clearly that A can be prescinded from B. Here are two examples (the first is Peirce's, the second is my own).[43]

Example 1. Suppose we began with a cubic polynomial, the general equation being

$$Ax^3 + Bx^2 + Cx + Dy = 0;$$

where $A = 1, B = 3, C = 2,$ and $D = -1,$ the equation is

$$y = x^3 + 3x^2 + 2x.$$

(See graph of cubic equation.)

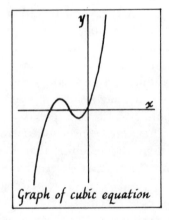

Graph of cubic equation

When $A = 0,$ the cubic equation degenerates into a second degree equation:

$$Bx^2 + Cx + Dy = 0.$$

Where $B = 3, C = 2,$ and $D = -1,$ the equation is

$$y = 3x^2 + 2x.$$

This is a parabola and represents the first order of degeneracy of a cubic equation.

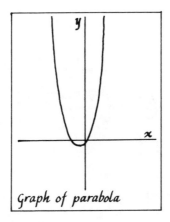

Graph of parabola

In the case where $D = 0$, the resulting equation is

$$x^3 + 3x^2 + 2x = 0;$$

the graph of which is three straight lines, representing the second order of degeneracy of the original cubic equation. (See graph of three straight lines.)

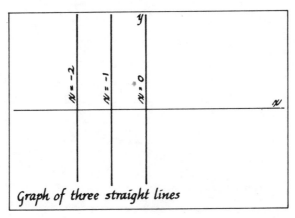

Graph of three straight lines

Example 2. Suppose we began with an ellipsoid, the general equation being

$$Ax^2 + By^2 + Cz^2 + D = 0.$$

The graph of $x^2 + 4y^2 + 16z^2 - 16 = 0$ is shown (see graph of ellipsoid).

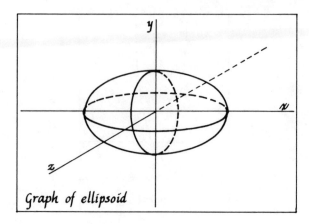

Graph of ellipsoid

If we let $C = 0$, the equation becomes

$$Ax^2 + By^2 + D = 0.$$

The graph of $x^2 + 4y^2 - 16 = 0$ shown; the original ellipsoid has degenerated into an ellipse (see graph of ellipse).

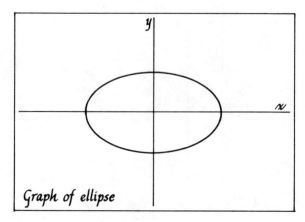

Graph of ellipse

If we let $D = 0$, the equation becomes

$$Ax^2 + By^2 = 0.$$

The only point that then satisfies the equation $x^2 + 4y^2 = 0$ is $x = 0$ and $y = 0$. The graph of $x^2 + 4y^2 = 0$ is shown (see graph of point [0,0]); the

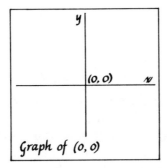

Graph of (0, 0)

ellipse has degenerated into a point. This condition of a second degree of degeneracy can be reached also directly from the ellipsoid by letting $D = 0$ in the quadric equation $Ax^2 + By^2 + Cz^2 = 0$. In $x^2 + 4y^2 + 16z^2 = 0$ the only point that will satisfy the equation is $x = 0$, $y = 0$, $z = 0$ (see graph of point [0, 0, 0]).

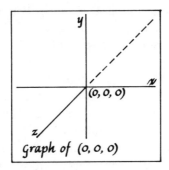

Graph of (0, 0, 0)

Peirce *used* this method of *prescission* to discover the natural classes of most general ideas. That is, Peirce used this method of prescission to discover classes of phanerochemical compounds and to order these into natural classes, thus doing for ideas what Mendeleyev's periodic table of the elements did for the chemical elements. We shall complete this chapter by giving an account of Peirce's main results.

That one of his results which is perhaps widest in scope is that in a sense there is only one phanerochemical element, namely *thirdness*.[44] What *is observed* is that thirdness can be prescinded from secondness, firstness, and every other idea which means that every other idea must be a further determination of a third. This result corresponds with his claim in semiotic that everything is, in a sense, a sign (see the following chapter).

Another result wide in scope is that *seconds* and *firsts* may be considered as *phanerochemical elements* as long as it is understood that these are *degenerate thirds*.

A third result is that since thirdness, secondness, and firstness are prescindable from every other idea, every other idea must be a third, second, and first, whatever else it is, and may therefore be assigned a valency of 3, 2, or 1, depending upon which category is dominant in the idea.[45] Another way to put this result would be to say that *every* idea other than the idea of thirdness itself is in some sense a degenerate third.

If thirdness, secondness, and firstness are considered phanerochemical elements, then together they form a phanerochemical compound. This compound, like all phanerochemical compounds, is a class and a system. This compound is a system by virtue of having two constraints on it. These constraints are not anything Peirce invented; they are observables. These constraints are: (1) that a third cannot be a further determination of a second or a first; and (2) that a second cannot be a further determination of a first. In what follows, I shall refer to these two constraints as the *phanerochemical bonding constraints*.

Any given phanerochemical compound (whether it be comprised of thirdness, secondness, and firstness, or of less indeterminate ideas) is a compound of the phanerochemical elements 1, 2, 3 and may be represented accordingly with a sequence of these numbers. In representing these compounds, we follow the convention of keeping the higher valencies to the left in the sequence. Thus, typical phanerochemical compounds may be represented as, say, 21 or 31 or 211 or 33221. Phanerochemical bonding constraints rule out the number sequences 23, 13, and 12. The ordered juxtaposition 23 is not possible because a third cannot be a further determination of a second; for example, a triadic relation cannot be a further determination of a dyadic relation. The sequence 13 is not possible because a third cannot be a further determination of a first; for example, the perceiving of a red color cannot be a further determination of the red color itself. And the sequence 12 is not possible because a second cannot be a further determination of a first; for example, the contrast between one red color and another cannot be observed by looking at just one of the reds or by initiating a further determination of that red by, say, making it a brighter red.

Since thirds are generated from three factors, there is nothing in that circumstance which prevents a third from being a further determination of some other third. For example, the idea that A is badly welded to B is a further determination of the idea that A is welded to B. Since a second is generated from two factors, there is nothing preventing a second from being a further determination of another second. For example, a sudden gush of water may be further determined to have been caused by a sudden breaking of a water pipe. Since a first is generated by one factor, there is nothing preventing a first from being a further determination of another first. For example, the idea of the color mercuric iodide red represents a further determination of the idea of the color red. Thus classes of compounds may have the structures 33 or 22 or 11. Since seconds and firsts are further determinations of thirds, compounds of the form 32 and 31 are possible. And since firsts are further determinations of seconds, 21 is also possible. In summary, the possible compounds of two ideas are: 33, 32, 31, 22, 21, and 11; and the impossible compounds are 23, 13, and 12.

These possible classes of compounds (33, 32, 31, 22, 21, 11) are natural classes because they represent an ordered sequence of all possible kinds of further determinations as offspring of the idea of thirdness. The same is true of *any* phanerochemical compound. To give a few examples, consider the compounds 33111, 3333, 322, and 3222. The first of these, 33111, is exemplified by the following sequence of thoughts: the idea of *being*, followed by the idea of *being* a quality, followed by the idea of a *quality*, followed by the idea of the *quality black*, followed by the idea of the *quality of this black* right before me. Peirce discussed this example (not at the time as an example of a phanerochemical compound) in "On a New List of Categories" of 1867. There, he argued that the idea of *being* or *predication* itself permitted an "indefinite determinability."[46] The sequence 3333 represents a phaneron such as the following: consider the idea that sea salt (NaCl) and oil of vitriol (H_2SO_4) produce the spirit of sea salt (HCl) and Glauber's salt (Na_2SO_4). Looked at as the *idea* of one thing producing a second, this idea is a 3: looked at as involving *first* the idea of some combination yielding some result, *second* NaCl combining with H_2SO_4, *third* 2Na combining with SO_4, and *fourth* H combining with Cl, the idea is a 333. If we attend to the circumstance that as the Glauber's salt and the spirit of sea salt are formed they *separate* from each other, the idea becomes 3332. The compound 322 may be exemplified as follows: consider the idea that the sun attracts the earth. Looked at as some dyadic relation, this idea is a 2; the attraction looked at in itself is a dyadic relation which is a second relative to another kind of dyadic relation; Peirce called this attraction itself a dynamic relational dyad which is ordered, and this type of 2 is a second relative to essential dyads such as color and red color.[47] Thus if we consider the idea that the sun attracts the earth and this gives rise to the idea of the attraction itself, the formula for that compound is 22. But on the other hand, if we look at *A attracts B* as a further determination of the triadic relation that *A determines B*, then *this* idea becomes a degenerate third, 322. In other words, *first* there is the idea of one thing determining another, *second* there is the idea of a kind of determination called attraction, *third* the sun attracting the earth is a case of this. An example of the compound 3111 would be this: the idea that the spectral colors red, green, and violet can be combined to result in any desired color may be viewed as a law, which is a third.[48] If the combinations are viewed as contiguous but independent wave motions, these are seconds and the idea becomes 3222. If the combined qualities are emphasized, the idea is a 3111.

Every phanerochemical compound is a natural class in the sense that every phanerochemical compound represents a phaneron in which each idea is a further determination of the idea which preceded it. But Peirce *ordered* all these phanerochemical compounds and referred to the higher classes in this ordering as *the natural classes*. This completed his phanerochemistry as far as he carried it out. Since every class is a third or a degenerate third, the system must be ordered in obedience to that principle, which amounts, simply, to the recursive application of the phanerochemical bonding constraint to each generation of 3's, 2's, and 1's as these emerge from *the* (one) *parent three*. Trying to express in words how the system of natural classes *springs up* from the idea of thirdness is *not a good way to describe* the growth of natural classes of ideas. Peirce tried it and here is the result:

> Taking any class in whose essential idea the predominant element is Thirdness, or Representation, the self-development of that essential idea—which development, let me say, is not to be compassed by any amount of mere "hard thinking," but only by an elaborate process founded upon experience and reason combined—results in a *trichotomy* giving rise to three sub-classes, or genera, involving respectively a relatively genuine thirdness, a relatively reactional thirdness or thirdness of the lesser degree of degeneracy, and a relatively qualitative thirdness of thirdness of the last degeneracy. This last may subdivide, and its species may even be governed by the three categories, but it will not subdivide,

in the manner which we are considering, by the essential determinations of its conception. The genus corresponding to the lesser degree of degeneracy, the reactionally degenerate genus, will subdivide after the manner of the Second category, forming a catena; while the genus of relatively genuine Thirdness will subdivide by Trichotomy just like that from which it resulted. Only as the division proceeds, the subdivisions become harder and harder to discern.[49]

The only way to see how natural classes *spring up* (and thus to *understand* what Peirce has in mind) is to diagram several generations of threes, twos, and ones stemming from one *parent 3* and settling into families by obeying the phanerochemical bonding constraints. The system works (or grows?) as follows.

A single, *parent 3* produces a first generation.

parent	first generation
3	3
	2
	1

Since there are no previous relatives in this sequence, no ideas to the right in the sequence, the result after the first generation are the following three natural classes.

(1) 3
(2) 2
(3) 1

The *parent 3* then produces a second generation but the only real families will be those which obey the bonding constraints, which leaves six natural classes after the second generation.

parent	second generation	natural classes from first generation (in triplicate)	natural classes after second generation
3	3	3	(1) 3 3
	$\begin{bmatrix} 3 \\ 3 \end{bmatrix}$	2	(2) 3 2
		1	(3) 3 1
	2	3	----
	$\begin{bmatrix} 2 \\ 2 \end{bmatrix}$	2	(4) 2 2
		1	(5) 2 1
	1	3	----
	$\begin{bmatrix} 1 \\ 1 \end{bmatrix}$	2	----
		1	(6) 1 1

The one *parent 3* then gives birth to a third generation which, after obeying the bonding constraints, settles down to ten natural classes.

parent	third generation	natural classes from second generation (in triplicate)	natural classes after third generation
3	3	3 3	(1) 3 3 3
	3	3 2	(2) 3 3 2
	3	3 1	(3) 3 3 1
	3	2 2	(4) 3 2 2
	3	2 1	(5) 3 2 1
	3	1 1	(6) 3 1 1
	2	3 3	------------
	2	3 2	------------
	2	3 1	------------
	2	2 2	(7) 2 2 2
	2	2 1	(8) 2 2 1
	2	1 1	(9) 2 1 1
	1	3 3	------------
	1	3 2	------------
	1	3 1	------------
	1	2 2	------------
	1	2 1	------------
	1	1 1	(10) 1 1 1

The next *offspring,* obtained in exactly the same way, are these fifteen quadruplets.

(1) 3 3 3 3
(2) 3 3 3 2
(3) 3 3 2 2
(4) 3 3 3 1
(5) 3 3 2 1
(6) 3 3 1 1
(7) 3 2 2 2
(8) 3 2 2 1
(9) 3 2 1 1
(10) 3 1 1 1
(11) 2 2 2 2
(12) 2 2 2 1
(13) 2 2 1 1
(14) 2 1 1 1
(15) 1 1 1 1

Peirce said that we find in Pythagoras the beginning of a true science of the categories.[50] Peirce referred to one of his own ideas as *the ceno-pythagorean idea: it is the idea of phanerochemical valency.*[51] As Aristotle has informed us, the basic Pythagorean principles were the *unlimited* and the *limited.*[52] Imagine a clear stretch of sandy beach and imagine drawing a triangle in the sand. This triangle is not the result of placing three pebbles on the sand: it is the result of limiting the unlimited in a particular way. *After* the vertices are formed, we can imagine placing pebbles at the vertices and in that way representing this particular limitation upon the unlimited by the number three. In the Pythagorean system all things were thought of as numbers or as like numbers. Numbers, in turn, were formed by limiting the unlimited in a particular sacred way. While we do not know what that was, it may have been by constructing triangle after triangle upon a first triangle, as illustrated.

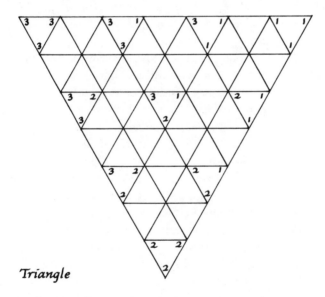

Triangle

If we start with the bottom triangle (which happens to be labeled 222) and add successive strips above it, the number of vertices which develop are represented by the Pythagorean or triangular numbers, which are 1, 3, 6, 10, 15, 21, 28, 36, 45, 55, 66, etc. Without bonding restrictions, the numbers of combinations of two elements is 3^2 of three 3^3 of four 3^4, etc.; when bonding restrictions are considered, the possible classes of ideas of these varying lengths is the same as the Pythago-

rean numbers (the same as the number of ordered triplets in the case
of compounds of three elements).

Peirce used the diagram above in describing his division of signs
into ten classes.[53] We do not know what he had in mind in using this
particular diagram, though it represents ten possible classes of phanerochemical compounds (or signs) with space in between for further
determinations, similar to a spectrum of lines representing chemical
elements with space in between the lines which represent potential
additional lines. The number sequence represented in Peirce's phanerochemical spectrum is identical to Boltzmann's representation of a
sequence of energy levels ($h\nu$, $2h\nu$, $3h\nu$) wherein the total number of
microstates, Ω, is equal to the sum of the series of triangular numbers
up to that point. Herbert Schneider mentions that Peirce's treatment
of the categories seems sometimes playful and at best experimental—
that Peirce often analyzed by threes for the fun of it.[54] Peirce wrote,
"So prolific is the triad in forms that one may easily conceive that all
the variety and multiplicity of the universe springs from it."[55] Had
Peirce lived long enough he most emphatically would have incorpo-
rated the messenger RNA codons within his system of triples.

Peirce was not carried away by number magic. His natural classes of
phanerochemical compounds *are* natural classes because they obey the
bonding constraints, which means that they are classes that are really in
accord with our *logica utens*. Peirce considered the kind of work he was
doing on the categories and on the field of ideas as radically different
from the kind of work Hegel was doing on the categories. Peirce said
that in Hegel's case, Hegel gets the next category in order simply by
calling out "Next!"[56] When Peirce suggests that his system of logic
(having in mind the entire system, but with emphasis upon the originalian end of the system) is virtually generally held,[57] he has in mind the
circumstance that we all use the system upon the occasion that we *think*
about anything because to think is to be bound by the laws of thought
which are the natural classes of ideas. While almost every book written
on Peirce mentions his distinction between *logica utens* and *logica docens*,
not a great many of these books emphasize the fact that Peirce considered *logica utens* not simply a bunch of ideas, but a "system of logic
all made."[58] The system of general ideas or our *logica utens* is isomorphic with the logic of relations in the sense that important general ideas
have identifiable counterparts or analogues in the logic of relations.
For example, a counterpart to the idea of *continuity* is the *illative rela-*

tion; a counterpart to the idea of further *determination in depth* is *logical multiplication* (or *intersection*); a counterpart to the idea of further *determination in breadth* is expressed in terms of *universes of discourse,* and *indices;* a counterpart to the idea of *symmetry* is the idea of an *inverse function.*

The relationship between Peirce's phaneroscopy and his logic of relations resembles the relationship between the various constituents in a chemical system. When a chemist writes a chemical equation of the form $AB + CD \rightleftarrows AD + BC$, he is expressing the fact that the reaction runs both ways at once. It is not that the logic of relations is based upon phaneroscopy or the other way around: the two aspects of Peirce's system of logic mutually influence each other. Although the results of phaneroscopy are "eminently fallible,"[59] at the same time it is important to "realize that the very best of what we, humanly speaking, know [we know] only in an uncertain and inexact way,"[60] (relative to exact logic itself). In the next chapter the main lines of Peirce's phanerochemistry are gone over using the terminology of semiotic or the theory of signs. The terminology of semiotic is especially useful for making clearer the important notion of phanerochemical valency.

III

SPECULATIVE GRAMMAR (3)

In his Presidential Address to a 1979 joint meeting of the Semiotic Society of America and the Charles S. Peirce Society, Max Fisch raised the following question: "Just *how* general is Peirce's general theory of signs?" Fisch's answer, briefly put, was, "so general as to entail that, whatever else anything may be, it is also a sign."[1]

Suppose I wake up in the morning and notice that it is getting light outside: that is a sign to me that the sun is rising. Suppose I observe that a magnet orients itself along a meridian: that is a sign to me of a magnetic field running in a general north-south direction at that point. Peirce gave the example of how the marks left on a fence by tramps are understood by other tramps as signs that the people who live in that district have such and such an attitude toward tramps.[2]

A sign is potentially, if not in fact, a member of an infinite sequence of signs. Peirce defined a sign as follows:

> A sign stands *for* something *to* the idea which it produces, or modifies. Or, it is a vehicle conveying into the mind something from without. That for which it stands is called its *Object;* that which it conveys, its *Meaning;* and the idea to which it gives rise, its *Interpretant.* The object of a representation can be nothing but a representation of which the first representation is the interpretant. But an endless series of representations each representing the one behind it may be conceived to have an absolute object at its limit. The meaning of a representation can be nothing but a representation. In fact, it is nothing but the representation itself conceived as stripped of irrelevant clothing. But this clothing never can be completely stripped off; it is only changed for something more diaphanous. So there is an infinite regression here, too. Finally, the interpretant is nothing but another representation to which the torch of truth is handed along; and as representation, it has its interpretant again. [Lo] another infinite series.[3]

Other definitions Peirce gave of a sign are:

A *Sign* or *Representamen,* is a First which stands in such a genuine triadic relation to a Second, called its *Object,* as to be capable of determining a Third, called its *Interpretant,* to assume the same triadic relation to its Object in which it stands itself to the same Object.[4]

Anything which determines something else (its *interpretant*) to refer to an object to which itself refers (its *object*) in the same way, the interpretant becoming in turn a sign, and so on *ad infinitum.*[5]

I define a sign as anything,—be it an existent thing or actual fact, or be it, like what we call a "word," a mere possible form to which an audible sound, visible shape, or other sensible object may conform to, or be it a property or habit of behaviour of something either experienced or imagined,—which is on the one hand so determined (i.e. affected either by causation or through the medium of a mind) by an object other than itself and on the other hand, in its turn so affects some mind, or is capable of doing so, that this mind is thereby itself mediately determined by the same object.[6]

A Sign is a Cognizable that, on the one hand, is so determined (i.e. specialized, *bestimmt*), by something *other than itself,* called its Object (or, in some cases, as if the Sign be the sentence "Cain killed Abel," in which Cain and Abel are equally Partial Objects, it may be more convenient to say that that which determines the Sign is the Complexus, or Totality, of Partial Objects. And in every case the Object is accurately the Universe of which the Special Object is member, or part), while, on the other hand, it so determines some actual or potential Mind, the determination whereof I term the Interpretant created by the Sign, that that Interpreting Mind is therein determined mediately by the Object.[7]

In 1867 Peirce described three classes of signs which arise from the circumstance that symbolic sign-action cannot be prescinded from an interpretant, that indexical sign-action cannot be prescinded from the idea of a dyadic relation, and that iconic sign-action is prescindable from all correlates. The three resulting classes of signs are symbols, indexes, and icons, respectively.[8] Iconic semiosis or sign-action is the representing of the object of the sign by resembling the object. Indexical semiosis is representation by actual connection with the object, as, for example, by being the physical effect of the object. Symbolic semiosis is representation or signification by virtue of being so understood, and that by nature or by convention. In 1903 he described ten classes of signs and introduced these by first describing ordered triadic relations.[9] In 1906 he described three classes of signs which arise from the circumstance that semiosis is iconic or indexical or symbolic, and said that this is only one of ten different divisions of signs.[10] In 1908, in describing these ten different divisions, he pointed out that by trichotomies they lead to 3^{10} or 59,049 *a priori* combinations of ideas to consider, which, when ordered, reduce to 66 basic possible classes of signs.[11]

Regardless of the number of respects in which signs are considered—this number giving the number of classes at hand, whether ten or sixty-six or whatever—that respect which is of overriding importance is the type of semiosis or sign-action involved, which is the semiotic analogue of the idea of phanerochemical valency. In describing the ten classes which result from considering signs in three respects, Peirce wrote that the most fundamental division is according to the manner of signifying;[12] and in 1908 he wrote that he divided signs into ten trichotomies *"governed* by the three categories of Valency."[13]

The three different kinds of semiosis, symbolic, indexical, and iconic, correspond to the valencies of 3, 2, and 1 respectively and these occur amidst an environment of different kinds of objects, signs, and interpretants. Peirce introduced his 1903 classification of signs (into ten classes) by first discussing triadic relations and then describing signs as a subcase of triadic relations.

Triadic relations are relations which involve three correlates. At 2.235 Peirce distinguished between a First Correlate, a Second Correlate, and a Third Correlate and defined these as follows:

> The First Correlate is that one of the three which is regarded as of the simplest nature, being a mere possibility if any one of the three is of that nature, and not being a law unless all three are of that nature. The Third Correlate is that one of the three which is regarded as of the most complex nature, being a law if any one of the three is a law, and not being a mere possibility unless all three are of that nature. The Second Correlate is that one of the three which is regarded as of middling complexity, so that if any two are of the same nature, as to being either mere possibilities, actual existences, or laws, then the Second Correlate is of that same nature, while if the three are all of different natures, the Second Correlate is an actual existence.[14]

If each correlate is classified as a first, second, or third, this gives 27 possible combinations. If these are *ordered,* the result is ten classes of triadic relations which correspond exactly to the ten classes of phanerochemical compounds of three elements described above, except that the order now becomes

(1) 1 1 1
(2) 1 1 2
(3) 1 2 2
(4) 2 2 2
(5) 1 1 3
(6) 1 2 3
(7) 1 3 3
(8) 2 2 3
(9) 2 3 3
(10) 3 3 3

A footnote in the *Collected Papers* at 2.236 states that the order of First Correlate and Third Correlate should be reversed, but this footnote jumps the gun because Peirce brings about the reversal the editors want when *he* changes the order (of First Correlate and Third Correlate) at 2.242. It is not until we *name* the classes of *signs* that the object *as understood* (the Third Correlate of the original triad) becomes the simplest member of a triad (and therefore a First Correlate).

At 2.239 Peirce mentioned a second division of triadic relations, one depending on the "dyadic relations" between (1) First Correlate and Second Correlate, (2) First Correlate and Third Correlate, and (3) Second Correlate and Third Correlate. No matter how one construes these relations, no matter how one combines the ten classes of each division together, and no matter how one orders any given triad, the possible classes of *ordered* triadic relations turns out to be ten. The result as it applies to triadic bonding is that we can consider the "dyadic bonds" between First Correlate and Second Correlate, between First Correlate and Third Correlate, and between Second Correlate and Third Correlate, on equal footing with correlates in describing classes of triadic relations. And when this is applied to signs, it permits our treating a relation between, say, a sign and its object as a triadic relation with one of the correlates being the type of sign-action involved.

The transition from divisions of triadic relations to divisions of signs takes place in the pivotal passage at 2.242 which runs:

> A *Representamen* is the First Correlate of a triadic relation, the Second Correlate being termed its *Object,* and the possible Third Correlate being termed its *Interpretant,* by which triadic relation the possible Interpretant

is determined to be the First Correlate of the same triadic relation to the same Object, and for some possible Interpretant. A *Sign* is a representamen of which some interpretant is a cognition of a mind.[15]

The most important thing, here, is that what is a Third Correlate and an interpretant in the original triad becomes the First Correlate in the subsequent "naming" triad.

In his division of signs into ten classes, Peirce considered: (1) what kind of thing a sign was interpreted to signify; (2) what kind of semiotic action was involved; and (3) what kind of sign was involved. Relative to *this* triad, the original interpretant (that is, the Third Correlate of the original triadic relation) is the First Correlate; the kind of sign-action is the Second Correlate; and the final naming of the kind of sign is the Third Correlate.

For example, suppose a strip of litmus paper is observed to turn blue when dipped into a solution of sodium hydroxide. This is a sign to me that the percentage of hydrogen ions in this solution is minimal. The object of the sign is the percentage of hydrogen ions; the sign itself is the blue strip of litmus paper in this context; the interpretant of the sign is my understanding that this blue strip of litmus paper represents the percentage of hydrogen ions in the solution and that this is minimal. *This interpretant,* the Third Correlate of this original triad, can now serve as the First Correlate in a subsequent triad and does so serve in that subsequent triad used to name the kind of sign involved in the original triad. In order to name this kind of sign, Peirce would go on to consider: (1) what kind of object the sign was understood to signify (the original Third Correlate), which in this case would be an existent thing, the percentage of hydrogen ions in the solution; (2) what kind of sign-action was involved, which in this case is indexical; and (3) what kind of thing the sign itself was, which in this case was an existing thing, the blue litmus paper in this context.

When a sign is understood to be the sign of a first, *that* interpretant leads us to call the sign a *rheme* (also *seme*). When a sign is understood to be the sign of a second, *that* interpretant leads us to call the sign *dicent*. When a sign is understood to be the sign of a third, *that* interpretant leads us to call the sign an *argument*. Signs themselves may be firsts, seconds, or thirds: these Peirce calls *qualisigns, sinsigns,* and *legisigns,* respectively.

Six of Peirce's ten classes of signs are *rhemes.*[16]

(1) *Rhematic Iconic Qualisigns* (111). Suppose a quality, magenta, resembles another quality, a more saturated magenta. I understand that the magenta signifies the more saturated magenta iconically by resembling it. What the magenta signifies is a first; the signifying is iconic and magenta itself is a qualisign. If we say, simply, that this kind of sign is a *qualisign,* that is sufficient to distinguish rhematic iconic qualisigns from the other nine classes of signs. This is not true of the label *rhematic* or the label *iconic.* Unfortunately, this circumstance may mislead the reader into thinking that the kind of thing a sign is in itself is the dominant consideration in classifying signs. That *qualisign* is the most *economical name* for this kind of sign should be taken for what it is and not taken as an indication that what class a sign is put in is basically a function of what kind of sign it is in itself. As we proceed through the classes, it will become clear that the type of semiosis is the main factor, in conjunction with a consideration of the kind of object the sign is understood to signify, in the identification and naming of classes of signs.

(2) *Rhematic Iconic Sinsigns* (112). Suppose I have before me *this* double helix model which I understand to represent *some* organic compound. That the model represents some as yet to be determined organic compound means that it represents a possibility which is a first and so understood this model is a rheme. That the structure of the model resembles the structure of DNA or other organic compounds means the semiosis is iconic. That the model is an actually existing thing is ground for calling it a sinsign. The most economical label is *iconic sinsign,* since all icons are rhemes.

(3) *Rhematic Iconic Legisigns* (113). Suppose I see the following marks on a page in a book:

$$\begin{array}{ccc} \text{H} & \text{O} & \\ | & \| & \\ \text{H}-\text{C}-\text{C}-\text{O}-\text{H} \\ | & & \\ \text{H} & & \end{array}$$

I understand that this represents some sort of organic compound and so I classify the sign as a rheme. Its action is iconic. As an existent it is a sinsign. If I think of the *type* of which this is a replica, that is, if I think of it *as* a kind of thing organic chemists write down, then the sign viewed in that way is a type and is called a legisign. The most economical label is *iconic legisign*.

(4) *Rhematic Indexical Sinsigns* (122). Suppose that as I watch an aircraft land it suddenly flips over and crashes! *Something* caused it. This event points to a possible cause. The sign is thus a rheme and its action is indexical. Since the event exists, it is a sinsign. The most economical name is *rhematic indexical sinsign*.

(5) *Rhematic Indexical Legisigns* (123). Suppose I think of a type of ghost which is called a spectral ghost.[17] Replicas of such ghosts point to anomalies in the rulings of gitter plates or some such cause. The object of the sign is such possibilities and so the sign is a rheme. The sign action is indexical. As a *type* the sign is a legisign. Another example would be the idea that a thermometer is the type or kind of instrument that points to any one of a range of possible temperatures. Peirce's example is the demonstrative pronoun as a type, tokens of which point to unspecified possibilities. The most economical name is *rhematic indexical legisign*.

(6) *Rhematic Symbolic Legisigns* (133). A concept, the *concept black,* for example, is understood to be a sign of certain possibilities and is therefore a rheme. It operates symbolically and is a legisign. The most economical name is *rhematic symbolic*.

Signs understood to refer to seconds are called dicent signs (also *dicisigns* and *phemes*). These can be indexical or symbolic.

(7) *Dicent Indexical Sinsigns* (222). That a strip of litmus paper turns blue upon the occasion of my dipping it into a solution of sodium hydroxide may be taken as a sign of existing hydroxide ions in the solution and so understood the object of the sign is an existent and the sign is a sinsign. The action is indexical and the sign itself exists. The most economical label is *Dicent Sinsign*. The hydroxide ions thought of as possibilities which are pointed to by the sign make the sign, in this respect, a rhematic indexical sinsign.

(8) *Dicent Indexical Legisigns* (223). The kind of instrument which is called a barometer can point to a specific existing air pressure. Thought of as a kind of instrument influenced directly by an existent, this idea is a *dicent indexical legisign*. Of course if I attend to the circumstance that the barometer currently before me now reads 76 centimeters, the sign (given that I understand barometers and the context) is a

token and not a type and therefore the kind of sign involved is a sinsign and not a legisign. The most economical label is *dicent indexical legisign.*

(9) *Dicent Symbolic Legisigns* (233). Suppose a fact is symbolized by a *proposition,* for example, *this stove is black* or *this metal is lithium.* The object of the sign is an existent; its action is symbolic; and as a type it is a legisign. The most economic label is *dicent symbolic.*

Signs understood to refer to thirds are called arguments (also *delomes*).

(10) *Argument Symbolic Legisigns* (333). A law is symbolized by an inference such as, if the temperature of this kind of gas is increased (within a certain range) and the volume occupied by this gas kept constant, then the pressure would increase. This refers to a law. It operates symbolically and as a type is a legisign. Its most economical label is *argument.*

For the purpose of economizing thought, the ten classes of signs may be thought of as three kinds of *symbolizing,* two kinds of *indexing,* and one kind of *iconing* (plus four variants). The symbolizing is of thirds (such as laws), seconds (such as an existing state of affairs), or firsts (such as conjecture); the indexing is of seconds (such as *this* cause) or of firsts (such as *some* cause); and the iconing is of firsts (such as a possible shade of blue). What does the indexing may be a token as well as an index, which adds two variants; and what does the iconing may be an existent and/or a token, which adds two more variants. The three kinds of symbolizing would be 33 (3), 23 (3), and 13 (3); the two kinds of indexing would be 22 (2) and 12 (2); and the basic kind of iconing would be 11 (1). The two variants of indexing would be 22 (3) and 12 (3); and the two variants of iconing would be 11 (2) and 11 (3).

Peirce distinguishes between interpretants which are feelings, those which are actions, and those which are kinds of ideas or recurring patterns of idea clustering. These three kinds of *interpretants* are called *emotional, energetic,* and *logical,* respectively. The *logical interpretants* are of most importance for purposes of understanding Peirce's system of logic.

Suppose I see the setting sun as an orange disc in the west; this orange disc so understood is the *immediate object* of the sign (the immediate object may be potential or actual). The sun itself, whatever it is, is the *dynamic object*. Of course, we know the dynamic object only to the extent that we are capable of representing it as the interpretant develops. What Peirce called the *immediate interpretant* is the *potential* that a sign itself has to be understood (in such and such a way); we learn of this potential upon the occasion that we become acquainted with the sign.

Suppose the turning blue of a strip of litmus paper is a sign understood by me to be a sign of some property of the solution before me, but I know not what property; a chemist could come up with a sequence of further interpretants such as that this solution is basic, that the change in color of the paper was due to a change in the dye which was caused by the hydroxide ions in the solution, that these dyes work only within a certain range, etc. Peirce gave an example of this sort of development of the interpretant of the sign *lithium:*

> If you look into a textbook of chemistry for a definition of *lithium,* you may be told that it is that element whose atomic weight is 7 very nearly. But if the author has a more logical mind he will tell you that if you search among minerals that are vitreous, translucent, grey or white, very hard, brittle, and insoluble, for one which imparts a crimson tinge to an unluminous flame, this mineral being triturated with lime or witherite ratsbane, and then fused, can be partly dissolved in muriatic acid; and if this solution be evaporated, and the residue be extracted with sulphuric acid, and duly purified, it can be converted by ordinary methods into a chloride, which being obtained in the solid state, fused, and electrolyzed with half a dozen powerful cells, will yield a globule of a pinkish silvery metal that will float on gasolene; and the material of *that* is a specimen of lithium.[18]

These sorts of developments of signs are the sorts of interpretants which would be quite commonly found among the thoughts of chemists. This sort of interpretant is what Peirce called a *normal interpretant.* In principle the normal interpretant should be thought of as a potential sequence of signs which is of scientific interest because it is a logical sequence which determines the object of the sign more and more as inquiry continues. In the long run this sequence would represent the object as fully and as well as it should ever be represented; that is, it will be a maximal determination of the object. The long run interpretant is what Peirce called the *final interpretant.* The object as represented in the final interpretant is the *real, dynamic object* of the sign.

Peirce's ten classes of signs might well be arranged with *argument symbolic legisigns,* 333, at the top of the list and *rhematic iconic qualisign,* 111, at the bottom, similar to our earlier arrangement of phanero-chemical compounds of three elements. Such an arrangement has the advantage of reminding us that *symbolic* sign action is the only genuine semiosis and that indexical and iconic sign action are degenerate forms. This is not to disparage indexes or icons. Peirce wrote: "Of signs there are two different degenerate forms. But though I give them this disparaging name, they are of the greatest utility, and serve purposes that genuine signs could not."[19]

Speculative grammar seeks to discover the possible classes of signs and the fundamental forms of semiosis. As we have seen, the kind of semiosis is a major factor in determining the classes of signs. The classes of signs—as far as we have made them out—are a part of a system of signs and this essentially a semiotic system, and this essentially a system of *symbols.* Of what service to science is this system? Let us suppose that the goal of inquiry is to understand the universe, to render it more intelligible, to give a *rational* account of it, to find its *logic.* What is logical? What is rational? In Peirce's view it is a system of signs with the idea of a symbol at its head, and idea itself most indeterminate but yet capable of indefinite determination. *This,* Peirce wrote, "is the correct and logical manner of beginning an account of the universe."[20]

While Peirce never completed his system of signs, it is obvious that he intended to represent every possible idea as a further determination of symbolic sign action. The overall synechistic suggestion of originalian logic, from the point of view of semiotic, is the suggestion that every idea it is possible for us to have results from the further determination of symbolic semiosis and these further determinations are ordered along a continuum, proceeding by trichotomy in accord with the principle that there are three fundamental kinds of semiosis if we include the two degenerate forms. Thus we anticipate, as ideas of service to science, three natural classes of arguments, one fundamental class and two degenerate classes; we anticipate three classes of sciences and an ordering of the sciences in such a way that the laws or principles of each science represent further determinations of the sciences which are above it; we anticipate three fundamental kinds of laws and we anticipate that as we approach the maximally determined world of things, such as atoms, that these, too, will be understood, if understood well, as signs—which is not to say that peculiar properties do not emerge in the limit. In short, everything is a sign and everything a part of a *system of signs*.

Given that the two degenerate forms of Argument are signs representing seconds and firsts, respectively, it is anticipated that in the first generation there would be one fundamental mode of reasoning with two degenerate modes. The three natural classes of signs involved are Argument (333), Dicent Symbolic (233), and Rhematic Symbolic (133), which are the three main classes of Legisigns. Peirce characterized the parent class (333) as representing thirds or law-like classes of inferences which always or for the most part lead to the truth (deductions).[21] He characterized the first degenerate class (233) as "a method of forming Dicent Symbols concerning a definite question."[22] (The definite question would be a question such as the following: what proportion of apples in this barrel are red apples? The Dicent Symbol formed might be "The proportion of red apples is 25/100." This Dicent Symbol is formed on the basis of inductive procedures.) He characterized the second degenerate class, 133, as representing firsts, mere possibilities, such as the conjectures of abduction (or originalian logic).[23]

IV

CRITICAL LOGIC (1)

Suppose I pass sunlight through an inexpensive plastic prism and throw the solar spectrum on a wall. And suppose what I observe are the three colors, red, green, and blue. At this point I might estimate that the spectrum is comprised of three basic colors. Suppose I substitute a better prism and improve my experimental setup and then observe six colors—red, orange, yellow, green, blue, and violet. At this point I might estimate that the spectrum is comprised of six basic colors. An analogous thing happens at the transition point between originalian logic and critical logic. At one point originalian logic observes three natural classes of legisigns, namely, 333, 233, and 133 (argument symbolic legisigns, dicent symbolic legisigns, and rhematic symbolic legisigns). What originalian logic estimates, at this point, is that there are three fundamental modes of reasoning—deduction, induction, and abduction. According to observations made in originalian logic (admittedly these are not to be given much weight relative to critical logic), the natural offspring of these three classes of legisigns are the six classes 3333, 2333, 1333, 2233, 1233, and 1133 (this generation was represented in chapter 2 in the reverse order). At this point, then, originalian logic would estimate that there are six basic modes of reasoning. These are: three kinds of deduction, two kinds of induction, and one kind of abduction. While this originalian conjecture was by no means the only consideration Peirce took into account in his natural classification of arguments, he gave six natural classes of arguments in his critical logic—three kinds of deductions, two kinds of induction, and one kind of abduction. The three kinds of deductions are corollarial deductions (3333), deductions involving probability (2333), and theorematic deductions (1333). The two kinds of inductions are quantitative inductions (2233) and qualitative inductions (1233). In this chapter I shall first describe the three kinds of deductions and then describe *the* fundamental logical relation, the *illative* relation. In the next chapter I shall describe quantitative and qualitative induction. Not much more will be said about abductions (1133) because these have already been described in originalian logic.

Peirce thought of the various modes of reasoning as a system of inferences continuous in itself and, as I have indicated, continuous with the natural classes of ideas of originalian logic. The system of inferences studied in critical logic ranges from the strongest (corollarial deduction) to the weakest (abduction). Deduction, Peirce said, should be studied first;[1] it is, in the way I have indicated, the natural parent of all the weaker forms of inference and it is, Peirce said, the *rationale* for induction and abduction.[2]

(1) *Corollarial Deduction.* Corollarial deduction involves the colligation of premisses and other information, the construction of diagrams, experimentation upon these diagrams, and the observation and generalization of results.[3] A very simple example of a corollarial deduction would be to infer from the premiss $(x + y) + z$ the conclusion $x + (y + z)$ in accordance with the associative rule for arithmetic.[4] One of Peirce's examples of a corollarial deduction is as follows:

Suppose we are given an equation of the form

$$x^2 + 2Bx + C = 0$$

and we know that one solution or root is x_1. Are there any other possible solutions to this equation? Consider this set of equations:

$$x^2 + 2Bx + C = 0$$
$$x_1^2 + 2Bx_1 + C = 0.$$

Concerning this set of equations Peirce wrote:

> *Diagram* is a word which will do for any visual skeleton form in which the relations of parts are perspicuously exhibited, and are distinguished by lettering or otherwise, and which have some signification, or at least some significance. A system of equations written under one another so that their relations may be seen at a glance may well be called a diagram. Indeed any algebraical expression is essentially a diagram.[5]

Continuing on, subtraction yields—

$$x^2 - x_1{}^2 + 2Bx - 2Bx_1 = 0$$
$$x^2 - x_1{}^2 + 2B(x - x_1) = 0$$
$$(x + x_1)(x - x_1) + 2B(x - x_1) = 0$$
$$(x + x_1 + 2B)(x - x_1) = 0$$

So, we observe that under these conditions either $(x - x_1) = 0$ or $(x + x_1 + 2B) = 0$, and we could go on to further possibilities, for example, if $C = B^2$, then $x = -B$.

A popular contemporary view of deductive logic is that the essence of deduction is captured in axiomatic systems. These systems consist of a list of primitive symbols and logical operators, a recursive definition of well-formed formulas, a set of axiom *schemata,* a number of rules of inference (Peirce's formal leading principles such as "transformation permissions") and a set of theorems. First order systems are functionally and deductively complete and the set of axiom *schemata* is minimal. These axiomatic systems well illustrate many aspects of what Peirce had in mind by corollarial reasoning,[6] but not the experimental aspects of the trial and error search for proofs.

Hume expressed the opinion that the sciences of geometry, algebra, and arithmetic were comprised of propositions such as *the square on the hypotenuse is equal to the sum of the squares on the other two sides,* or *three times five is equal to half of thirty,* and that since mathematics was made up of such intuitively clear or demonstrable propositions, that mathematical reasoning was essentially "intuitively or demonstratively certain."[7] The reader should note the prominence in Hume's examples of the relation of *identity*. Kant defined an analytic proposition as a proposition the predicate of which was contained in the subject. *All bodies are extended* was, in Kant's view, an analytic proposition because we cannot think of *body* without thinking of *extension*. Peirce suggested that Kant could have put the analytic-synthetic distinction as follows: "if the proposition could be reduced to an identical one by merely attaching aggregates to its subjects and components to its predicate it was an analytic proposition; but otherwise was synthetic."[8] Supposing that all bodies were extended, it could be maintained that *all bodies* were identical to *however so much of extended things were bodies*. This is the Boolean line which we shall return to shortly. Were Kant's definition of *analytic* so modified, Peirce would agree that in that sense many cases of *corollarial* mathematical reasoning were analytic. For example the famous

case of $7 + 5 = 12$, which Kant took to be synthetic, Peirce took to be
analytic in the sense that it can be reduced to the form $0 + 0 = 0$
simply by defining numbers such as 7 as $G6$ where G stands for "next
greater than" and understanding that $G(x + y) = Gx + y = x + Gy$, as:[9]

$$7 = G6$$
$$12 = G11$$
$$Gx + y = G(x + y)$$
$$7 + 5 = 12$$
$$G6 + 5 = G11$$
$$\ldots \text{(etc.)}$$
$$x + Gy = G(x + y)$$
$$0 + G4 = G4$$
$$\ldots \text{(etc.)}$$
$$0 + 0 = 0$$

Kant maintained that the idea of *extension* is contained in the idea of
body. Peirce disagreed with this particular example on the grounds that
we do not necessarily think of body as extended because we may alternatively think of body as a field of forces, following the path of
Boscovich.[10] In any case, *analyticity*, as Kant defined it, involves the
notion that the predicate is in some sense contained in the subject;
further, Kant sometimes wrote as if we immediately see this when we
entertain the idea of the subject. Both Kant and Peirce would agree
that mathematics is not essentially analytic in this sense. Kant would
agree because he thought mathematics was comprised of synthetic
judgments involving constructions in space. Peirce would agree because
the theorems of number theory, for example, are not contained in the
postulates of number theory in the sense that these theorems are
readily seen to follow from these postulates when these postulates are
entertained.

Corollarial deductions are the strongest kinds of reasoning because
they are grounded upon observations of seconds in the sense that when
we represent the premises we are thereby compelled to represent the
conclusion. Mathematical or other diagrammatic deductions are, Peirce
wrote, "only observations of the mind's own constructions, but they
often have that *startling* quality which indicates that they *are* observations."[11] If several top mathematicians check a proof, that proof is very
likely free of error; whatever is proved is nevertheless considered sub-

ject to error and to review and may require subsequent revision. Even our mathematical results—the best and clearest we have—are not certain. Peirce did not view deduction as a chain of inferences each link of which is indubitable, but rather as a procedure which resembled a cable in that any strand might be defective, but the overall strength is reliable.[12]

Corollarial deductions are by no means restricted to being mathematical deductions. It is true that experimentation with the objects of mathematics is usually more economical than experimentation with physical objects, for in mathematics, Peirce said, one can learn almost as fast as one can write.[13] But when a physicist or chemist or biologist or any other experimentalist proceeds to manipulate his "alembics and cucurbits"[14] and to observe the results, this is not essentially different from the manipulation of mathematical symbols.[15]

> One of the leading mathematicians and mathematical philosophers of our age, Klein, gives another of those instructive comments upon mathematical procedure of which we have enjoyed a number from his pen. He again dwells, as he had already done, upon the importance of attentive intuition—in other words, of the *observation* of diagrams and the like—as an essential element of mathematical reasoning. Considering that mathematicians have long held that mathematics covers all exact reasoning, quantitative or not, it will be seen that Klein is going over to a logical doctrine which has had defenders in this country and in England. According to this, our assurance that $(2 \cdot 4 \cdot 6 \cdot 8 \cdot 10) \div (1 \cdot 2 \cdot 3 \cdot 4 \cdot 5) = 2^5$ is of the same nature as our assurance that sulphuric acid is precipitated by baryta, we having satisfied ourselves in each case that a single experiment is sufficient; only in one case we observe Nature, in the other our own construction.[16]

(2) *Deduction Involving Probability.* Deductions involving probability may be calculations of *a priori* probabilities, such as calculating the *a priori* probability of getting a straight flush dealt from a deck of 52 cards. Since there are five cards in a normal poker hand, the total number of possible poker hands is

$$52!/(5!(52 - 5)!) = 2,598,960.$$

Of these possible hands 40 are straight flushes, so that the probability of getting a straight flush is

$$40/2,598,960 = 1/64,974.$$

But what Peirce called *probable deduction proper* were deductions involving *a posteriori* or frequency probabilities.[17] For example, if it is known that half of a *very large number* of apples are red, then we conclude deductively that as this population is sampled probably and approximately half of the sample would be observed to be red apples in the long run.

(3) *Theorematic Deductions.* A deduction is a theorematic deduction if the reasoner introduces an originary or theoric step,[18] an idea not contained in the original premises or contextual information; something, Peirce said, which neither the definition of the object of research nor anything yet known about the initial set of ideas suggest, although these leave room for the originary idea.[19] If a diagram is involved then some circumstance connected with the purpose which first prompted the construction of the diagram contributes to the determination of the permissible transformation that actually gets performed.[20] He described theorematic deduction further as follows.

> In the theorems, or at least in all the major theorems, a different kind of reasoning is demanded. Here, it will not do to confine oneself to general terms. It is necessary to set down, or to imagine, some individual and definite schema, or diagram—in geometry, a figure composed of lines with letters attached; in algebra an array of letters of which some are repeated. This schema is constructed so as to conform to a hypothesis set forth in general terms in the thesis of the theorem. Pains are taken so to construct it that there would be something closely similar in every possible state of things to which the hypothetical description in the thesis would be applicable, and furthermore to construct it so that it shall have no other characters which could influence the reasoning.[21]

> Mathematics is the science which draws necessary conclusions. Such was the definition first given by my father, Benjamin Peirce, in 1870. At that day the new mathematics was in its early infancy and the novelty of this definition was disconcerting even to the most advanced mathematicians; but today no competent man would adopt a definition decidedly opposed to that. The only fault I should find with it is that if we conceive a science, not as a body of ascertained truth, but, as the living business which a group of investigators are engaged upon, which I think is the only sense which gives a natural classification of sciences, then we must include under mathematics everything that is an indispensable part of the mathematician's business; and therefore we must include the *formulation* of his hypotheses as well as the tracing out of their consequences. Certainly, into that work of formulation the mathematicians put an immense deal of intellectual power and energy.

Moreover, the hypotheses of the mathematician are of a peculiar nature. The mathematician does not in the least concern himself about their truth. They are often designed to represent *approximately* some state of things which he has some reason to believe is realized; but he does not regard it as his business to find out whether this be true or not; and he generally knows very well that his hypothesis only approximates to a representation of that state of things. The substance of the mathematician's hypothesis is therefore a creature of his imagination. Yet nothing can be more unlike a poet's creation. The reason is that the poet is interested in his images solely on account of their own beauty or interest as images, while the mathematician is interested in his hypotheses solely on account of the ways in which necessary inferences can be drawn from them. He consequently makes them perfectly definite in all those respects which could affect the ways in which parts of them could or [could] not be taken together so as to lead to necessary consequences. If he leaves the hypotheses determinate in any other respects, they are hypotheses of *applied* mathematics. The pure mathematician generalizes the hypotheses so as to make them applicable to all conceivable states of things in which precisely analogous conclusions could be drawn. In view of this I would define Pure Mathematics as the science of pure hypotheses perfectly definite in respects which can create or destroy forms of necessary consequences from them and entirely indeterminate in other respects.[22]

Everybody knows that mathematics, which covers all necessary reasoning, is as far as possible from being purely mechanical work; that it calls for powers of generalization in comparison with which all others are puny, that it requires an imagination which would be poetical were it not so vividly detailed, and above all that it demands invention of the profoundest. There is therefore, no room to doubt that there is *some* theoric reasoning, something unmechanical, in the business of mathematics. I hope that before I cease to be useful in this world, I may be able to define better than I now can what the distinctive essence of theoric thought is.[23]

An example of theorematic deduction is a well-known problem in topology called "The Seven Bridges of Königsberg." Leonhard Euler (the man to whom Peirce gives credit for having invented logical diagrams)[24] described the problem as follows:

The problem which I understand is quite well known, is stated as follows; In the town of Königsberg in Prussia there is an island A, called "Kneiphof," with the two branches of the river (Pregel) flowing around it, as shown in [the illustration]. There are seven bridges . . . crossing the two branches. The question is whether a person can plan a walk in such a way that he will cross each of these bridges once but not more than once. I was told that while some denied the possibility of doing this and others were in doubt, there were none who maintained that it was actually possible. On the basis of the above I formulated the following very general problem for myself; Given any configuration of the river and the branches into which it may divide, as well as any number of bridges, to *determine* whether or not it is possible to cross each bridge exactly once.[25]

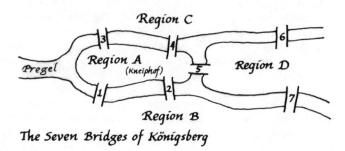

The Seven Bridges of Königsberg

By introducing a series of new ideas not contained in the original statement of the problem, Euler solved not only this problem but all others like it. The first new idea he introduced was to diagram a journey through a number of regions according to the order in which each region is entered, regardless of which bridge is used. For example, a journey from region *B* (in the illustration) to region *A* across either bridge is diagrammed *BA*. If a journey goes from region *A* to region *B* to region *C*, it is diagrammed not as *ABBC*, but simply as *ABC*. If a journey were to begin in region *B*, cross four bridges, and end in region *D*, its corresponding diagram would be the following form.

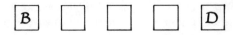

If any journey ends where it begins (see circular diagram), its diagram would nevertheless be of the same general form.

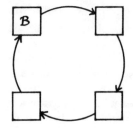

Let N equal the total number of bridges crossed in a journey. The diagram which corresponds to any journey which crosses every bridge exactly once must meet the condition that the number of occurrences of letters in it must equal $N + 1$. An individual region is classified as an *odd* region if an odd number of bridges enters it. An individual region is classified as an *even* region if an even number of bridges enters it. Suppose an individual region A is an odd region entered by, say, five bridges (see figure).

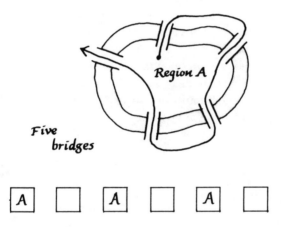

In the description or diagram of the crossing of these five bridges the letter A must occur three times whether the journey begins in A or outside of A, as the actual tracing of a few such paths show. Suppose an individual region A is an even region entered by, say, four bridges (see figure).

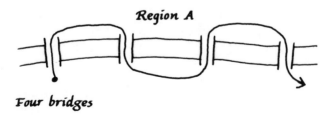

In the diagram representing the crossing of these bridges the letter A occurs two times if the journey begins outside A, and three times if it begins inside A. In general, if A is an odd region, the number of occurrences of letters required in a diagram of the crossing of its bridges equals $(n + 1)/2$, where n is the number of its bridges. If A is an even region the number of letters required is $n/2$ if the journey begins outside A, and $(n/2) + 1$ if the journey begins inside A.

The description of a complete journey must meet both regional and overall conditions, so that the *sum* of the number of necessary occurrences of letters for each region must equal $N + 1$, the total number of occurrences of letters in the diagram representing the entire journey.

Given any network of regions and bridges, we can label the regions A, B, C, etc., count the total number of bridges, N, and calculate the number of occurrences of each letter as required in the diagram of the crossing of its bridges. Since the overall journey must begin in one and only one region, there can be at most only one need to use the $(n/2) + 1$ calculation, so we shall deal with that separately *after* tabulating all other results. The tabulation of information and the calculations for any given network may be put in the following convenient form:

$N =$ ___

Column I	Column II	Column III
(a list of regions)	(a list of the number of bridges, n, entering each region)	(required occurrences of letters for regional diagrams)

For example, in the case of the seven bridges of Königsberg, the information is tabulated as follows:

$N = 7$

Column I	Column II	Column III
A	5	3
B	3	2
C	3	2
D	3	2

Another example might have fifteen bridges (see illustration).

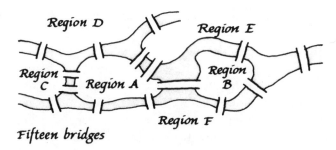

Fifteen bridges

The corresponding tabulated information for fifteen bridges would be:

$N = 15$

Column I	Column II	Column III
A	8	4
B	4	2
C	4	2
D	3	2
E	5	3
F	6	3

In gathering the information for *Column II* each bridge is, considering the entire network, counted twice. So if any *Column II* entry is odd, there must be an even number of such entries. The result is that there are only two kinds of tables that can occur: the kind where all *Column II* entries are even numbers and the kind where there are 2, 4, 6, 8, etc., odd-numbered *Column II* entries. This second kind subdivides into two cases, giving three cases altogether:

Case 1: *If all Column II entries are even,* the *column II* sum will equal *N*. But if all the entries are even, the journey must begin in an even region which increases the *column III* sum by one, in which case this sum is equal to *N* + 1 and *the journey is possible.*

Case 2: *If there are exactly two odd-numbered entries in Column II,* then the *column III* sum will equal *N* + 1 and *the journey is possible* . . . provided it begins in an odd region, for if it begins in an even region the *column III* sum would be increased by one, in which case it would equal *N* + 2.

Case 3: *If there are more than exactly two odd-numbered entries in Column II,* then the *column III* sum will be greater than *N* + 1 and *the journey is impossible.*

The Seven Bridges of Königsberg falls under *case 3* and so this journey is impossible. The fifteen-bridges example given above falls under *case 2* and so this journey is possible if and only if it begins in region *D* or region *E*. Euler's solution well illustrates what Peirce had in mind by theorematic deduction because Euler introduces a series of new ideas which are not general ideas, but ideas expressed in specific terms, using letters and diagrams, and at all points capturing as economically as possible the main relations involved in the problem.

We know that Peirce was a mathematician, that he had a great deal of respect for the methods of mathematics, and that he sought to make every science as exact as mathematics. Carolyn Eisele has always maintained that Peirce's work in philosophy and logic developed out of his work in mathematics and science and can be understood properly only in this context.[26] Recently it has been suggested that this thesis of Eisele's is now so well established that we ought to refer to it as *Eisele's law*.[27] We know, also, that it is *mathematics* which stands at the head of Peirce's classification of the sciences (see chapter 7), not logic, not semiotic, not speculative grammar, not critical logic, not transuasional logic. But on the other hand, mathematics in at least one important respect depends on logic. The respect in which mathematics depends on logic may be seen by attending to Peirce's distinction between a science (mathematics) which draws necessary conclusions and the science (logic) of drawing necessary conclusion.

Mathematics was often defined by Peirce as the *science which* actually *draws necessary conclusion*.[28] Mathematics has no need of the other sciences because it deals with the necessities of a world of possibilities of greater scope than any of the other sciences. Mathematics can offer, for example, a number of alternative geometries, one of which real space might be a subcase. Mathematics has results to report, upon which the other sciences depend; and the methods of the successful sciences may be seen as subcases of the methods of mathematics involving, most prominently, diagrammatic experimentation and careful observation. Mathematics not only has results to report, but, Peirce noted, there is no science in which the rate of acceleration of discovery is so great and no "science but mathematics in which discovery seems to be becoming continually more and more fundamental."[29]

Logic was sometimes defined by Peirce as the science of *drawing necessary conclusions* in the sense that logic studies in detail how it is that one (such as a mathematician) goes about drawing a necessary conclusion.[30] Logic analyses inferences as minutely as possible. Now when a logician takes a close look at the drawing of necessary inferences, he notices that the hypotheses from which these drawings set out are always changing, and changing most commonly in the direction of greater generality. It is the business of the mathematician, Peirce said, to form new mathematical ideas such as the idea of the system of imaginaries and the idea of Riemann surfaces.[31] But it is not the business of the mathematician, Peirce noted, to investigate what kinds of hypotheses are possible for him to have.[32] The mathematicians, Peirce wrote, "content themselves with adopting such hypotheses as are manifestly possible."[33] It is the business of the logician to ask the following: "what are the different systems of hypotheses from which mathematical deduction can set out, what are their general characteristics, why are not other hypotheses possible and the like."[34]

Since by *logic* Peirce means a system of logic, and since this system includes originalian logic or phaneroscopy, it is obvious that phaneroscopy may well have a role to play in the generation of the kinds of theoric steps that are possible in theorematic deduction. Whether or not phaneroscopy is what Peirce has in mind when he speaks of a "higher kind of mathematics" is an interesting but as yet unanswered question.[35] It should be noted that even if mathematics does depend on phaneroscopy (or if it depends on the cenoscopic science of logic) in this one respect, mathematics is not thereby bumped out of its place at the head of the sciences. The sciences are classified according to which sciences for the most part and in general depend on which other sciences, and all the important and developed positive sciences depend on mathematics and not the other way around.

Returning to the language of semiotic, and with all three classes of deduction in mind, Peirce gave this definition of deduction: "A *deduction* is an argument whose interpretant represents that it belongs to a general class of possible arguments precisely analogous which are such that in the long run of experience the greater part of those whose premises are true will have true conclusions."[36] To say that deductions belong to a class of arguments *precisely analogous* is roughly equivalent to our contemporary distinction between arguments and argument forms, but must be understood to include standard forms of inferences as a limiting case of some degree of similarity. None of the three kinds of deduction is probabilistic in nature in the sense that the movement from premises to conclusion is merely likely or is in some other sense an inference whose leading principle is not a strong, standard form, the genesis of which goes back to and rests on obsistencies.

The Illative Relation. In Peirce's view the *most* general logical relation is the sign-relation. But relative to sign-relations which are arguments, the most general and fundamental logical relation is the *illative relation* or *illation*,[37] which is symbolized thusly: —<.

Peirce's father, Benjamin Peirce, was fond of writing on the blackboard the equation $\Sigma P \, \delta\rho = 0$. For Benjamin Peirce this fundamental equation of analytical machanics was packed full of meaning and significance.[38] For Charles Peirce the symbol for *illation* was packed full of meaning and significance. We shall unpack some of this meaning and significance for to do so sheds considerable light on what Peirce meant by deductive reasoning and rationality in general.

As useful as the *identity* relation is, it does not serve well to capture the essence of deduction. During the second half of the nineteenth century the most popular and respected view of the essence of mathematical or deductive reasoning was that of George Boole. Boole's system was based on the identity relation. He symbolized partial identities in the following manner: a proposition such as *All x is y* is symbolized as $x = uy$, where *uy* denotes whatever portion of the class *y* is identical to the class *x*. Suppose an argument has the form—

$$
\begin{array}{ll}
\text{All } x \text{ is } y. & (P1) \\
\text{All } y \text{ is } z. & (P2) \\
\hline
\text{All } x \text{ is } z. & (C)
\end{array}
$$

Boole symbolized this—

$$
\begin{array}{ll}
x = uy & (P1) \\
y = vz & (P2) \\
\hline
x = wz & (C)
\end{array}
$$

Boole devised a general method of showing in the case of valid deductions that the conclusion was in fact identical (or partially identical) to the premisses. This general method consists of a series of identities, partial identities, and algebraic manipulations divided into five basic steps. As applied to the above argument, these five steps are (1) the elimination of *u* from *P*1 and *v* from *P*2; (2) the reduction of the result to one equation; (3) the elimination of *y* from the reduced equation; (4)

expansion and solving for *x* in terms of *z* and (5) the interpretation of
the results. In detail, these five steps run along like this—

Step 1:
$$x = uy$$
$$x - uy = 0$$
$$f(u) = f(1) \text{ or } f(0)$$
$$f(1) = x - y$$
$$f(0) = x$$
$$f(1)f(0) = x(x - y) = 0$$
$$x^2 - xy = 0$$
$$x - xy = 0$$

therefore $P1 = x(1 - y) = 0$

and similarly $P2 = y(1 - z) = 0$

Step 2: Since *P*1 (with *u* eliminated) and *P*2 (with *w* eliminated) both obey
the law of duality, they can simply be added, yielding—
$$x(1 - y) + y(1 - z) = 0$$

Step 3: The elimination of y is effected as follows—[39]
$$y = 1 \longrightarrow f(xz) \text{ becomes } (1 - z)$$
$$y = 0 \longrightarrow f(xz) \text{ becomes } x$$
$$x(1 - z) = 0$$
$$x = 0/(1 - z)$$

Step 4: $x = 0/(1 - z)$
$$x = (0/0)z + (0/1)(1 - z)$$

Step 5: We drop the constituent with the 0/1 coefficient and interpret the
0/0 coefficient to read "an indefinite class," so that $x = wz$ reads,
"the class *x* is identical with the intersect of *z* and an indefinite
class, *w*, i.e., that *x* is some part of *z*."

The algebraic moves required in the course of the five steps in this and
in all other cases are based upon the following six identities—

(1) $xy = yx$
(2) $xy = x$ (where *y* denotes what *x* denotes)
(3) $x + y = y + x$
(4) $z(x + y) = zx + zy$
(5) $z(x - y) = zx - zy$
(6) $(x = y) = (zx = zy)$

which, in turn, reveal the laws of thought. The expression $xy = yx$
reveals that in thinking of the intersection of two classes we get the

same result no matter which class we think of first. For example, to think of red apples as apples which are red is *identical* to thinking of red apples as red things which are apples. (Peirce would disagree, of course, with this.) The thought which each of the other algebraic laws reveals is not difficult to imagine except for the expression $xy = x$ (where y denotes what x denotes). This expression presumably reveals that to think of the same class a second time adds nothing new to the original thought; however, the expression is more fundamental than it looks, Boole maintained, because it is equivalent to the law of contradiction by virtue of the equivalencies—$[(xx = x) = (x^2 = x)] \equiv [(x - x^2) = 0] \equiv [x(1 - x) = 0].$[40]

In 1896 Peirce reported that since 1867 he had maintained that there was but one primary and fundamental logical relation and that was *illation*.[41] In 1870 he introduced the symbol $\prec$ which at that time he said he took to be another way of writing $\leqslant$.[42] By 1880 he was calling $\prec$ "illation."[43] Illation is similar to material implication or the *consequentia de inesse* insofar as $A \prec B$ means not-A *vel* B. But $A \prec B$ should be read, "in any possible case, i, either Ai is not true or Bi is true."[44] To write $S \prec P$ is to indicate that if the idea S is forced on the mind, then the idea P is definitely forced on the mind (by way of obsistencies).[45]

The illative relation is involved in the idea of an inference from premisses to conclusion, in the idea of a proposition or dicisign and in the idea of a term. Peirce wrote:

> By thus identifying the relation expressed by the copula with that of illation, we identify the proposition with the inference, and the term with the proposition. This identification, by means of which all that is found true of term, proposition, or inference is at once known to be true of all three, is a most important engine of reasoning, which we have gained by beginning with a consideration of the genesis of logic. In consequence of the identification in question, in $S \prec P$, I speak of S indifferently as *subject, antecedent,* or *premiss,* and of P as *predicate, consequent,* or *conclusion.*[46]

In the development of his thought which resulted in his seeing the nature and importance of the illative relation, Peirce was influenced by something which was implicit in Mill's analysis of the syllogism and explicit in DeMorgan's analysis of the syllogism, namely, the fundamental importance in reasoning of the *transitive relation*.

Mill claimed that the principle of reasoning was the *nota notae*.[47] Consider the syllogism:

All men are mortal.
Socrates is a man.
_____
Socrates is mortal.

Roughly speaking, being mortal is predicated of men and being a man is predicated of Socrates; however, it is not classes which are involved, but characteristics or marks. The marks of mortality are predicated of the marks of men and the marks of men are predicated of Socrates. Putting it in the singular for simplicity, the mark of a mark is a mark of the thing itself, that is, *nota notae est nota rei ipsius.* Since this principle does not involve classes, it is not the *dictum de omni et nullo,* the latter being the principle that whatever is true of a class is true of every member of that class.

Having considered Mill's view and others, Peirce wrote that the statement of the validity of *Barbara* "has been called the *dictum de omni,* the *nota notae,* etc., but it is best regarded after DeMorgan, as a statement that the relation signified by the copula is a transitive one."[48]

What DeMorgan had pointed out was that while "is" (or "is not") is the copula of standard-form categorical propositions, the validity of a syllogism like *Barbara* built up out of such propositions depends not on the *identity relation* but rather on the *transitive relation;* "is" is a kind of transitive relation and it is on the grounds of this relation that *Barbara* is valid.[49] A syllogism with the copula "is greater than" is (when otherwise analogous to *Barbara*) also valid, since "is greater than" is also a transitive relation. Peirce frequently expressed the sentiment that we owe a lot to DeMorgan for being the thinker who really opened up the logic of relations.[50]

It is important to notice that the illative relation, when understood in all its magnificence, makes reference to firsts, seconds, and thirds. This circumstance makes $\prec$ well suited to symbolize reasoning. Suppose that as a part of a proposition or argument, the reasoner's intention is to make reference to a class of things, such as to the class (A) of men. That is, he plans to begin his assertion or inference, A $\prec$ .... The subject *A* in this context, or the antecedent, refers to a class of things. But a class of things is an *ens rationis,* for the being of a class of things consists in the existence of whatever of all that is possible has such and such a quality.[51] Given any *x*, if that *x* has such and such a quality, then *x* is one of an indefinite number of existents which are members of the class signified by the subject term.

This is one respect in which possibilities or firsts are involved in the illative relation. When Peirce said that theorematic reasoning and other kinds work by *abstraction,* this reference to possibilities is one thing he had in mind.[52] Our conceptions *are* domains of possibility subject to generation by description and subject to further determination. Consider the proposition *All men are wise.* If one uses material implication, the proposition may be symbolized (*x*) (*Mx* $\supset$ *Wx*). It is not clear how to interpret this. Traditionally, the Philonian context does not contemplate anything beyond the existing state of things. But by using illation and writing the proposition $\prod x$ (*Mx* $\prec$ *Wx*), we make it clear that what was traditionally understood as a proposition *de inesse* should be understood as and is understood as a *modal* proposition; that is, this dicisign is understood as making reference to possibilities, necessities, and would-bes.[53] The quantifiers of dicisigns, along with their *indexes*, make it clear that it is seconds which force or control the validity of the inference, that is, it is actual existents which determine whether or not, supposing x is M that x is or is not W.[54] Consider the probable deduction that if half of a large population of apples are red and half yellow, as we sample this population the sample would show the same characteristics. This is put, using illation, that

$$\text{1/2 pop red and 1/2 yellow} \prec \text{1/2 sample red and 1/2 yellow}$$

meaning that if we were to have an indefinitely large population of half red and half yellow apples and if we were to continue to sample such a possible population, the results, the obsistent fact would be that we would hit upon this ratio in the long run. Peirce included ratios such as half along with the quantifiers and other indexical signs.[55]

In 1885 Peirce raised this question: What is the most useful way to interpret the hypothetical proposition?[56] His answer was, "Now, the peculiarity of the hypothetical proposition is that it goes out beyond the actual state of things and declares what *would* happen were things other than they are or may be."[57]

Consider the argument *All pendulum swingers are men,* therefore *All pendulum swingers are wise.* The premiss is "If anything were a pendulum swinger, then that thing would be a man." The conclusion is, "If anything were a pendulum swinger, then that thing would be wise." In order to be a complete argument, something material must be added to the argument. If we add the premiss, "If anything were a man, then that thing would be wise," the result is a complete argument. What we added in this case Peirce calls a material or extralogical leading principle.[58]

The standard analysis of the complete argument is effected by asserting that $[(x) (Px \supset Mx) \cdot (x) (Mx \supset Wx)] \supset (x) (Px \supset Wx)$. By universal instantiation the quantifiers are removed from the premisses; a matrix is used to show that $[(Py \supset My) \cdot (My \supset Wy)] \supset (Py \supset Wy)$; and by universal generalization the quantifier is put back in the prefix of the conclusion.

The corresponding Venn diagram is shown.

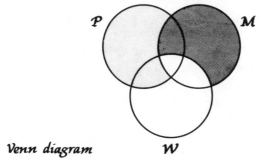

Venn diagram W

Peirce's analysis of the argument, the standard analysis, and the Venn diagram all make the point that this complete argument belongs to a class of inferences all of which are instances of valid logical form; that is, in Peirce's terminology, that this complete argument is one token of a type or a logical leading principle, $P \prec C$ (and, less generally, $A \prec B, B \prec C, A \prec C$). To say that there is a valid form is to say that for any instance we might possibly come across of that form, that instance would be a valid complete argument. None of the above analyses points out, simply, that from an existing state of affairs such and such another state is included; each indicates in its own way that such and such a possible state *would* generate such and such obsistencies. Ever since the slave-boy incident in the *Meno* it has been recognized that diagrams show things beyond themselves. While standard analyses do not make this clear, the inference really is *modal* in character. Consider the rule for universal instantiation; this rule comes closer to

Peirce's analysis if it is understood not simply that for any x there now is, it is now the case that such and such, but that for any x there *might* be, now or in the future, that x *would be* such and such. Further, were y such an x, then y would be such and such. The rule for generating the initial assignments in the matrix is this: the function 2^n gives us the number of possible combinations of two values there would be, where n is the number of variables and n ranges from 1 to positive infinity. And the rule for universal generalization states that if any random thing, y, were such and such, then everything would be such and such. Peirce put the point this way, the logical leading principle states, in effect, "that among all the states of things which can be supposed without conflict with logical principles, those in which the premiss of the argument would be true would also be cases of the truth of the conclusion;"[59] and, alternatively, "reasoning consists in the perception that if P is found true as it has been found true, then *must* C be always or mostly true; and this 'must' means that not only [is] C true (or probable) unless P is false (or not found true in the way supposed) but that every analogous premiss and conclusion are in the same relation."[60]

In Peirce's view, then, the observations in which the experimentation culminates are of the illative form and this reasoning is more than seeing that such and such is the case, it is seeing that if such and such were the case, then so and so would be the case. When we think of a collection, we may think of the actual members of the collection which Peirce called a *gath,* or we may think not of these but of a general description or rule or law or operation which signifies a collection, which Peirce called a *sam.*[61] One basic kind of collection is a finite collection, that is, what Peirce calls an *enumerable* quantity. What Peirce calls the "syllogism of transposed quantity" is a corollarial deduction such as—

> Every Hottentot kills a Hottentot.
> No Hottentot is killed by more than one Hottentot.
> _____
> Every Hottentot is killed by a Hottentot.[62]

The syllogism of transposed quantity applies to the *gath* of enumerable collections, and in regard to such collections nominalism is possible. Other basic kinds of collections are *denumerable* or indefinite collections such as the collection of positive integers and *abnumerable* collections such as the collection of irrationals. These infinite collections cannot be *gaths,* but can only be *sams.* The syllogism of transposed quantity does not apply to them.[63] Infinite collections, while not physically possible, are not logically impossible.[64] When we refer to the whole of a class, Peirce said, this does not necessarily mean the synthesis of the class is complete.[65] These collections are abstractions and can only be signified by *sams,* that is, they cannot be definitively or completely diagrammed and in regard to them nominalism is impossible.

It is not difficult to convince anyone that a point made pictorially about a triangle not only holds for that triangle, but would hold for other triangles. If so, then it is a "would be" that is involved. Suppose that a certain relation obtains between the set [*abc*] and the set [123], namely, the relation that for *a* there corresponds the number 1, for *b* there corresponds the number 2, and for *c* the number 3; further, suppose that for 1 there corresponds the letter *a,* for 2 the letter *b* and for 3 the letter *c.* In a case like this which is finite and of no particular interest it is the case that a modal "would be" is involved, but the diagram at hand is not such as to impress that fact upon the reader or to send his thought rushing ahead to analogous cases. What might be said is only that this example, this diagrammatic example of two sets being related in a certain way, does not do a very good job of illustrating that which is observed upon the culmination of experimentation. However, let us retain this same relation and take note of what we observe when this same relation obtains between two more interesting sets, the set of ordered pairs and the set of positive integers. The diagram might look like this:

What does this diagram show? It shows:

First: that ∀ positive integer, *x, E!* an ordered pair, such that *x* corresponds to *y.* (I.e., for any positive integer there might be, there would be a corresponding unique ordered pair.)

Second: that ∀ ordered pair, *x, E!* a positive integer, such that *x* corresponds to *y.* (I.e., for any ordered pair there might be, there would be a unique corresponding positive integer.)

Peirce, who was one of the first to make these kinds of observations, expressed the exact observation in his logic of relations as follows:[66]

First: that

$$\Sigma_\beta \prod_i \Sigma_j \prod_k \bar{q}_{Pi} \Psi r_{\beta ij} \cdot (1_{ik} \Psi \bar{r}_{\beta kj}) \cdot q_{Qj}$$

where P = positive integers and Q ordered pairs

Second: that

$$\Sigma_\beta \prod_i \Sigma_j \prod_k \bar{q}_{Pi} \Psi r_{\beta ij} \cdot (1_{ik} \Psi \bar{r}_{\beta kj}) \cdot q_{Qj}$$

where Q = positive integers and P ordered pairs.

When a mathematician or other experimentalist observes that under certain conditions such and such would happen, he is observing what Peirce sometimes called *experimental phenomena*—that is, for example, such things as the Brownian movement, Hall's phenomenon, Zeeman's phenomenon, Michelson's phenomenon, etc.[67] Given any laboratory, anywhere, under the right conditions certain occurrences *would be* observed. An interesting question is whether or not the distinction between *existents* and *would be's* is of any help in solving the paradoxes of the infinite. Peirce made some moves in that direction. For example, he pointed out that if Achilles really had to exert an infinite number of existent efforts of mind or body to catch the tortoise he could never do it, that is, he could not accomplish what today is called a super-task. But we know that he does catch the tortoise, so that he does not have to, he must not have to, accomplish a super-task. The only kind of infinity he passes over is a series of real possibilities, or what would be there for him to pass over, were physical points to exist and to correspond with the numbers on the real number line.[68]

Peirce cryptically referred to reasoning or philosophy or science or inquiry as being, in its least objectionable form, hyperbolic.[69] The hyperbola is distinguished from other elementary curves in that it involves the concept of an asymptote which cannot be defined (understood or thought of properly) without using the illation relation. (An hyperbola has two asymptotes.) The analogy between reasoning and the hyperbola is not original with Peirce. In Peirce's discussion of individuals (which is a discussion about inferences of course) we get a clue as to where he got the idea for there he refers to an appendix of Kant's "Transcendental Dialectic."[70] In that appendix Kant had pointed out that infinity is not something which actually exists, but is something which goes out beyond the possibility of experience; as far as pure reason is concerned, infinity must be considered an ideal, a regulative idea as opposed to a constitutive idea. In his discussion, Kant drew an analogy between the idea of infinity and the hyperbola and said that pure reason entertains this idea of infinity only asymptotically. A typical hyperbola is shown.

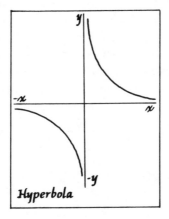

Hyperbola

If it is known that the *x*-axis is in fact an asymptote, then the asymptotic relations illustrated obtain.

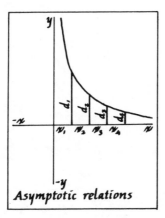

Asymptotic relations

For any positive integer, *n*, there would be a point x_n on the *x*-axis such that the distance between x_n and the hyperbola is less than $1/n$.[71] Thus the hyperbola represents a universal continuum of semiotic-action and emphasizes its recursive references to what under certain conditions would be the case.

There is no kind of reasoning or rationality essentially different from mathematical or deductive reasoning and, as Peirce put it, "to state wherein the validity of mathematical reasoning consists is to state the ultimate ground on which any reasoning must rest."[72] Other kinds of inferences are degenerate forms of deduction,[73] and the classes of signs other than legisigns are relatives of deduction since all ten classes of signs are offspring of Argument Symbolic Legisigns—these are vague relations of exact relatives of the form A —< B. The purpose of signs, Peirce reminds us, is to bring truth to expression; and the law under which a sign must be true is the law of inference. "Hence, the illative relation is the primary and paramount semiotic relation."[74]

V

CRITICAL LOGIC (2)

Contemporary logic texts usually distinguish between deductive and non-deductive arguments. In the case of valid deductive arguments, the premisses imply the conclusion, the argument is analytic and non-ampliative. In the case of good non-deductive arguments, the premisses supply some reasonable amount of evidence for the conclusion, additional evidence increases the strength of the argument, and the argument is said to be ampliative. The term *induction* has a variety of uses today; sometimes it is used to refer to arguments involving probabilities sometimes to Mill's methods, sometimes to analogical arguments, and sometimes it is used to refer to all non-deductive arguments of whatever variety. As I have indicated, Peirce classified arguments differently, he did not take deductive reasoning to be analytic, and, as I shall indicate, he had a different view of induction as well.

Having a system of logic, every part of the system depends on every other part of the system in some respect and any given part of the system may be seen, in this respect, as basic relative to the rest of the system. At times Peirce will be found saying abduction is basic, at times deduction, and at times induction. Abduction or originalian logic may be seen as the basic kind of inference by virtue of the circumstance that it is the only kind of inference which introduces new ideas into science. Because of this Peirce calls abduction the "sheet anchor of science."[1] We have seen that deduction is the basic form of inference in the sense that all other forms of inference are degenerate forms of deduction;[2] deduction, Peirce says, is the most *dyadic* of the three logics because it is constrained and controlled by obsistencies.[3] But there are respects in which induction, too, is the basic form of reasoning: Peirce referred to induction as the "highest and most typical form of reasoning"[4] and as the "highest type of reasoning."[5] Using Kantian terminology, Peirce raised this question:

Thus, we seem to be driven to this point. On the one hand, no determination of things, no *fact*, can result in the validity of probable argument; nor, on the other hand, is such argument reducible to that form which holds good, however the facts may be. This seems very much like a reduction to absurdity of the validity of such reasoning; and a paradox of the greatest difficulty is presented for solution.

There can be no doubt of the importance of this problem. According to Kant, the central question of philosophy is "How are synthetical judgments *a priori* possible?" But antecedently to this comes the question how synthetical judgments in general, and still more generally, how synthetical reasoning is possible at all. When the answer to the general problem has been obtained the particular one will be comparatively simple. This is the lock upon the door of philosophy.[6]

As I indicated above, there are two basic classes of inductions: quantitative inductions (2233) and qualitative inductions (1233). That these and the other four modes of reasoning can be assigned numbers which show their places in the natural classes of ideas accords with Peirce's claim that it was the categories which guided him through the maze of the natural classification of inferences.[7] Both kinds of inductions differ from deductions in the following respect: whereas a deduction claims that if *A* were the case, then *B* would be the case, inductions always put a question to nature, the answer to which can be investigated by sampling or by some other laboratory procedure and being either quantitative or qualitative in kind.

(1) Quantitative Inductions. The strongest kind of inductions are quantitative inductions.[8] These involve experimentation, observations of obsistencies, and other features common to deductions; quantitative inductions are very close relatives of probable deductions proper.[9] Concerning the close relationship between deductive forms and inductive forms, Peirce wrote:

> Most of our reasoning is not deductive. It does not result from the consideration of a world of possibilities, or states of things we do not know not to be true, but results from the observation of the course of events in experience. In other words, it results from the estimation of probabilities. Probability is closely allied to possibility: it has been called the negative measure of our ignorance. But possibility is much the easier conception; and therefore necessary reasoning must be considered first. Besides, it will be found that every nondeductive argument refers to a necessary consequence, upon which its validity depends.[10]

We indicated earlier, when discussing abduction, that the following forms were especially important in classifying arguments:

First Figure   2/3 of $A = W$
              This $S = $ from A
              _____
              2/3 of this $S = W$

Third Figure   This $S = $ from A
              2/3 of this $S = W$
              _____
              2/3 of $A = W$

Second Figure   2/3 of this $S = W$
               2/3 of $A = W$
               _____
               This $S = $ from A

Peirce wrote that "*probability* lends an importance to the three figures which modern logicians have not been willing to accord to them."[11] By inserting probability into the three figures of classical syllogisms, the suggestion arises that there are three natural forms of inference and that these are parts of one system of inferences.

Consider the probable deduction:[12]

$$2/3 \text{ of } A = W$$
$$\text{This } S = \text{ from } A$$
$$\overline{2/3 \text{ of } S = W}$$

This probable deduction is the parent or "explaining syllogism" of the induction which results from interchanging the major and the conclusion, namely

$$2/3 \text{ of } S = W$$
$$\text{This } S = \text{ from } A$$
$$\overline{2/3 \text{ of } A = W}$$

While qualitative induction takes on a certain importance by being a culminating stage of scientific inquiry, Peirce nevertheless thought of quantitative inductions as paradigmatic cases of induction. In the *Century Dictionary*,[13] Peirce contrasted the classical view of induction with his own view: he pointed out that while classical inductions were understood to infer from the observation that *every* member of a sample had such and such a character, in *his* view inductions should be understood to include inferences from the observation that a *certain proportion* of the members of a sample have such and such a character to the conclusion that that same proportion of the members of the population have that same character. Quantitative induction includes reasoning from sample to population whether probabilities are involved or not;[14] it is the strongest kind of induction there is;[15] and it is nearly continuous with probable deductions. Before going on to describe quantitative induction further, it will be helpful to pause to describe the late nineteenth-century view of induction against which Peirce set forth his own view of induction.

Precisely analogous forms are very important in deductive reasoning. No matter what variations independent variables go through, the key thing is the function or form of operation involved in the deduction. In the late nineteenth century, that function or operation which was of greatest importance from the point of view of classifying inductions was the function or operation called *inverse deduction*. Probability was typically involved in inverse deductions, and what Peirce fought against was the view of the "school of inverse probability." This school included Pascal, Bernoulli, Quetelet, Laplace, Euler, Ploucquet, Lambert, Boole, DeMorgan, and Jevons. With the general line of thought of this school in mind, Peirce said that what he is refuting is the *doctrine of inverse probability*.[16] Jevons said that in the case of those inductive inferences which are most commonly drawn in practice, the principle involved is the principle of inverse probability.[17] Jevons stated this principle as follows: "If an event can be produced by any one of a certain number of different causes, all equally probable *a priori*, the probabilities of the existence of these causes as inferred from the events, are proportional to the probabilities of the event as derived from these causes."[18]

Suppose the effect or event for which we seek the cause is a deck of 52 cards ordered as they usually are when one buys them, ace to king in each suit. *A priori* we impose on the situation the notion that there could have been two and only two causes for this orderly arrangement—that somebody intentionally ordered the deck that way, or that the deck fell into that order by chance. Suppose that out of every 52! times somebody intentionally tries to order a deck he succeeds all but once; and suppose that by chance the same thing happens only once. Upon these assumptions, the inverse probability that that person's intention is the cause is:

$$\frac{(52! - 1)/52!}{[(52! - 1)/52!] + [1/52!)} = \frac{(52! - 1)}{52!}.$$

Jevons gave the following classical example of an inverse induction involving probabilities.[19] Suppose there are three boxes, the first containing seven white balls and three black balls, the second four white and six black, and the third three white and seven black. A white ball is drawn from one of the three boxes and it is required to determine from which of the three boxes it came. The probability that it was drawn from the first box is:

$$\frac{7/10}{(7/10) + (4/10) + (3/10)} = \frac{7}{14}.$$

The probability that it was drawn from the second box is 4/14, and from the third, 3/14.

The standard nineteenth-century method of reducing data was based upon the mistaken notion that inverse deduction could be used to calculate the real probable error of a set of measurements. Peirce frequently criticised the method, most notably in his "On the Theory of Errors of Observation."[20] Consider, as an example of this standard method of reducing data, the chart of measurements of human reaction time which Peirce observed on August 3, 1872 (the reaction time as observed ranged from 0.119 seconds to 0.374 seconds; the second column represents the number of observations made of each reaction time).[21]

According to the law of errors, Peirce's errors ought to have these four features; (1) positive and negative errors are symmetrically placed on both sides of the true value; (2) the sizes of the errors range from $-\infty$ to $+\infty$; (3) small errors are very probable and large errors very improbable, in accordance with the function $y = ke^{-\Delta^2}$; and (4) since the probability of a distribution of errors is a function of the product of the probability of each individual error (a distribution being looked at as a compound event), the most probable distribution of errors will be that in which $\sum \Delta^2$ is minimal. In practice what is done to move from, for example, Peirce's observations (above) to the true value of reaction time, is to take the mean of the observations to be the true value and, under this assumption, to consider the residuals to be the actual errors.

Measurements of human reaction time

thousandths of seconds	observations	thousandths of seconds	observations	thousanths of seconds	observations
119	1	224	4	270	3
...	...	225	8	271	3
134	1	226	6	272	1
...	...	227	5	273	4
156	1	228	9	274	1
...	...	229	4	275	5
172	1	230	7	276	0
...	...	231	11	277	2
175	1	232	12	278	0
...	...	233	18	279	0
188	2	234	5	280	3
189	0	235	7	281	2
190	1	236	11	282	1
191	0	237	10	283	1
192	1	238	8	284	0
193	0	239	8	285	1
194	0	240	6	286	4
195	0	241	9	287	0
196	0	242	8	288	1
197	0	243	12	289	0
198	2	244	10	290	2
199	1	245	16	291	0
200	2	246	9	292	4
201	1	247	7	293	0
202	0	248	11	294	3
203	0	249	13	295	0
204	1	250	13	296	0
205	1	251	14	297	1
206	1	252	14	298	0
207	1	253	12	299	0
208	2	254	12	300	0
209	6	255	6	301	0
210	3	256	8	302	1
211	3	257	12	303	0
212	3	258	5	304	0
213	3	259	8	305	0
214	4	260	6	306	0
215	1	261	9	307	2
216	1	262	2	308	0
217	4	263	6	309	1
218	7	264	4	...	...
219	5	265	1	334	1
220	3	266	1	...	...
221	6	267	2	340	1
222	3	268	2	...	...
223	1	269	3	374	1

Where δ is the standard deviation, Δ the residuals, and n the number of observations, the above data gives the result:

$\delta = \sqrt{\Delta^2/(n-1)} = 0.0236$

Probable error $= (0.0236)(0.6745) = 0.0159$

Reaction time $= 0.243 \pm .0159$ sec.

The school of inverse probability took it that such calculations of probable error are calculations of what the probable error really is. They believed that random errors followed the "law of errors," and thus errors of different sizes had, so to speak, different "causes," these "causes" being represented by the area under the various intervals of the curve representing the law of errors. Jevons said that the law of errors rests upon a consideration of probable natural combinations and that there is no difference between talking about probable natural combinations and causes.[22] The difficulty with this very non-Peircean perspective is that there is no way of knowing whether or not the sample mean is identical to the population mean (the real mean, the true value of human reaction time), or of knowing whether or not the distribution of residuals really does represent the theoretical distribution of true errors. To use the method of least squares to assure an identity or as close a resemblance as possible between the two distributions involved amounts to no more than begging the question at issue.

In Boole's view of deduction, the identity relation was, as we have indicated, very important. When it came to reasoning involving probability, whether deduction or inverse deduction, both Boole and Jevons after him tended to see this reasoning involving probability as based upon the identity relation. Jevons wrote:

> The fundamental action of our reasoning faculties consists in inferring or carrying to a new instance of a phenomenon whatever we have previously known of its like, analogue, equivalent or equal. Sameness or identity presents itself in all degrees, and is known under various names; but the great rule of inference embraces all degrees, and affirms that *so far as there exists sameness, identity or likeness, what is true of one thing will be true of the other.*[23] [emphasis Jevons's]

Jevons often spoke of the *leave* of a law of nature. Suppose a law of nature is known. If we know the law, the *leave* of the law can be predicted. The *leave* of a law is what a law allows to happen; it is a certain set of possibilities which remain open after the requirements of the law are met. If we know the leave, the law can presumably be inversely deduced. The term *inverse* was a popular term in the nineteenth century (and still is): subtraction was spoken of as the inverse of addition, $1/x$ as the inverse of x, and integration as the inverse of differentiation. A modern example of this inverse deduction would be: given a function of two variables, p and q, to be, say, *TFTT* under the standard assignment of initial values, to find the shortest well-formed formula of a given type capable of expressing this function, an acceptable solution being $p \supset q$. Jevons gave an example of inverse deduction expressed in the symbolism of his version of Boolean algebra: suppose we took the possible combination of A and B and their complements to be AB, Ab, aB, and ab; suppose each of these combinations to be a possible state of nature; and suppose we are provided with the additional information that the identity $A = B$ really is a rule or law of nature. Under these conditions it follows that the law leaves AB and ab as possible states of nature since the other two *a priori* possibilities become contradictory in light of the law. Now, according to Jevons, the first thing to notice about inductions is that they are essentially inverse deductions. For example, given the combination AB as that which nature leaves, what law or rule must have governed the universe of discourse AB, Ab, aB, ab to have produced this leave? Whatever the law, it must have eliminated Ab and aB. If the list of *a priori* possible laws is restricted to certain simple identities, not permitting partial identities, then the possible laws are $A = B$, $A = b$, $a = B$, and $a = b$; $A = B$ eliminates Ab and ab; $a = b$ eliminates Ab and aB, so that the law responsible for the leave AB is either $A = B$ or $a = b$.[24]

There is some plausibility to the idea of an inverse probable deduction in cases where *a priori* the domain of what is not known to be impossible has been delimited; but such cases are rare, and generally inverse probable deduction cannot be used to infer the probability of the cause of an event because neither the possible causes of an event are known nor the probability, given a possible cause, that that cause would produce such and such an effect.[25] Further, as Peirce saw things, the school of inverse probability had no way to calculate the probability of *any* real event. The policy the school of inverse probability most frequently attempted to use was to set up rather arbitrarily lists of possibilities and then to suppose that whatever was equipossible was equiprobable. Peirce often made the point that the school of inverse probability gives itself away when it claims that the probability of an unknown kind of event is ½. For example,

> As a specimen of LaPlace's results I will mention something he deduces from his principle of the "également possibles" and which is copied into all the textbooks of the subject,—all the usual ones,—to this day. Namely LaPlace says that if a man on occasions entirely new to him sees a phenomenon equally new on every one of those occasions up to N occasions (N being any whole number) then the probability is $(N + 1)/(N + 2)$ that the same phenomenon will occur on the next such occasion. I say this is nonsense, that it is trying to conclude by mathematical reasoning that which requires a radically different kind of reasoning. And what proves that it is nonsense is that if $N = 0$ the probability is ½. That is to say that on a wholly new occasion it would be a reasonable thing to make an even bet that an unheard of event would take place. That is the nonsense that results from trying to reason mathematically on matters of fact on the basis of pure ignorance. LaPlace was renowned for lack of sound good sense, and his doctrine about these inverse probabilities shows it.[26]

Thus the conceptualist's method of treating probabilities which attempts to reduce all probabilistic inferences to deductions and to deductions involving *a priori* probabilities, Peirce concluded, fails.[27] Induction is not reducible to inverse deduction; induction is a different natural class of reasoning.[28]

Let us return, now, to Peirce's view of *quantitative induction*. Consider, again, the deductive form—[29]

$$\frac{\begin{array}{l} 2/3 \text{ of } A = W \\ \text{This } S = \text{from } A \end{array}}{2/3 \text{ of this } S = W}$$

and compare it with the inductive form—

$$\frac{\begin{array}{l} \text{This } S = \text{from } A \\ 2/3 \text{ of this } S = W \end{array}}{2/3 \text{ of } A = W}$$

Peirce pointed out that the deductive inference from *2/3 of the population is W* to *2/3 of S is W*, is *symmetrical* with the inductive inference from *2/3 of S is W* to *2/3 of the population is W*.[30] If is is known that a barrel of apples contains 2/3 red apples and 1/3 yellow apples, it is expected that samples of this would have the same ratio. And, going the other way, if 2/3 of a sample from a barrel of apples are red and 1/3 yellow, it is expected that the barrel of apples will have the same distribution of red and yellow apples. The logical relation which is at the center of attention in both the case of the first figure probable deduction and the third figure quantitative induction is whether or not the sample and population *represent* or are *signs* of each other.

In the case of a deductive inference from population to sample, we know in principle that the population parameters or characteristics would be represented by the parameters of a sufficiently large random sample. In the case of a quantitative induction, the strength of the corresponding deduction is approached to an extent which is a function of the extent to which a large random sample of a finite population can be obtained. Peirce was careful to limit quantitative induction to finite collections and he was careful in stating the conditions which must be met in order for a sample to represent or be a sign of a population.[31] For example—

> Suppose a ship arrives at Liverpool laden with wheat in bulk. Suppose that by some machinery the whole cargo be stirred up with great thoroughness. Suppose that twenty-seven thimblefuls be taken equally from the forward, midships, and aft parts, from the starboard, center, and larboard hold, and that these being mixed and the grains counted, four-fifths of the latter are found to be of quality *A*. Then, we infer, experientially and provisionally, that approximately four fifths of all the grain in the cargo is of the same quality.[32]

Of the various conditions which must be met in order for the sample to represent or be a sign of the population, the first is *predesignation*. The inquirer decides before observing his samples what characteristics he will be looking for and under what conditions he will look for them. Then he "proceeds to *experiment*, that is, to realize those conditions and watch for the predicted phenomena."[33] If the inquirer does not predesignate, then he runs the risk of producing *ad hoc* inferences concerning the marks of the population under investigation, that is, the sample would be biased and thus not represent the population. The Francis Baring example referred to by Goudge,[34] Cheng,[35] and others serves to illustrate the problem of not pre-designating and so we shall give that example again here.

In order to illustrate the necessity of this rule I take a random sample of eminent persons. It is quite a random one, for it consists of the first names on pages 100, 300, 500, 700, 900, of *Phillips's Great Index of Biography*. The names are as follows:

	Born		Died
Francis Baring	1740	1800	Sept. 12
Vicomte de Custine	1760	1794	Jan. 3
Hippostrates (of uncertain age)			
Marquis d' O.	1535	1594	Oct. 24
Theocrenes	1480	1536	Oct. 18

Now I might, in violation of the above rule of predesignation, draw the following inductions:

1. Three-fourths of these men were born in a year whose date ends in a cipher. Hence about three-fourths of all eminent men are probably so born. But, in fact, only one in ten is so born.

2. Three eminent men out of four die in autumn. In fact only one out of three.

3. All eminent men die on a day of the month divisible by three. In fact, one out of three.

4. All eminent men die in years whose date doubled and increased by one gives a number whose last figure is the same as that in the tens' place of the date itself. In fact, only one in ten.

5. All eminent men who were living in any year ending in forty-four died at an age which after subtracting four becomes divisible by eleven. All others die at an age which increased by ten is divisible by eleven.[36]

The classical *conditio sine qua non* for a reliable statistic is to have a large random sample. We *try* to obtain random samples by instituting well-designed methods of sampling and by varying these methods extensively.[37] That for which we aim Peirce defined as follows:

> The sample must be taken according to a precept or method which, being applied over and over again indefinitely, would in the long run result in the drawing of any one set of instances as often as any other set of the same number.[38]

> A sample is a *random* one, provided it is drawn by such machinery, artificial or physiological, that in the long run any one individual of the whole lot would get taken as often as any other.[39]

Whatever marks a very large, finite population may have, these marks have a good chance of being represented by a *large* random sample and *ceteris paribus* the larger the sample the greater the chance of represen-

tation. The central limit theorem is a proof to the effect that by indefinitely increasing the sample size, population parameters have very little
chance of not being truly represented.[40] An induction which meets all
these conditions is a very strong argument: its strength approaches that
of a probable deduction. Concerning such sample-population or quantitative inductions, Peirce wrote:

> An argument from a random sample, is a method of ascertaining what
> proportion of the members of a finite class possess a predesignate, or
> virtual predesignate, quality, by selecting instances from that class ac-
> cording to a method which will, in the long run, present any instances as
> often as any other, and concluding that the ratio found for such a
> sample will hold in the long run. Its justification is evident.[41]

Suppose, given the information that a shipload of wheat contains 4/5
quality A wheat, we proceed to observe samples of this shipload with
this known characteristic. The inference that the sample will eventually
exhibit this 4/5 ratio is a probable deduction: if we do not observe this
4/5 ratio at first, we know that in theory we would observe it in the long
run. Thus the conclusion of the probable deduction, namely, the conclusion that 4/5 is the ratio to be expected, gets *vindicated*, in principle,
in the long run.[42] *Vindication* consists in getting what you said you
would get and what the probable deduction concludes is that we would
get 4/5 in the long run.[43]

Suppose we investigate a large, finite population such as the load of
wheat, predesignate what characteristics constitute quality A wheat,
make every effort to obtain a large random sample, and obtain such a
sample. And suppose that at this point the sample is 4/5 quality A wheat
so that we estimate that the population is 4/5 quality A wheat. This
conclusion is not justified in the sense that is is *known* at this point or any
analogous point that the particular estimate made really does represent
the ratio of quality A wheat in the population or shipload of wheat.[44]
And this 4/5 ratio is not a ratio which we expect to be vindicated in the
long run. What can be said, and what Peirce said, is that as we go along
we *modify* this ratio so that it becomes true in the long run.[45] This is,
Peirce said, the marvelous feature of quantitative induction, that it is a
self-corrective *procedure*.[46] If we take a close look at a quantitative induction we see that the "justification of its conclusion is that that conclusion
is reached by a method which, steadily persisted in, must lead to true
knowledge in the long run of cases of its application, whether to the

existing world or to any imaginable world whatsoever."[47] It is important to note that when Peirce said that quantitative induction leads to the truth in any imaginable world whatsoever, he meant that it will discover whatever regularities or lack thereof there are in that world without presuming anything ahead of time about *these* regularities: this is not to say that no presuppositions of any kind are made, for the conditions of sampling large populations must be presupposed to apply. In the case of probable deduction, the anticipated result of sampling is calculated or otherwise given and the correct sampling procedure in principle would vindicate this ratio. In the case of a quantitative induction, the correct procedure would zero in on the truth in the long run and this kind of induction is "valid" only in the sense that the correct procedure would work or, one may say, the validity of a quantitative induction is contingent and depends upon whether or not the correct procedure is being followed. Peirce put it this way:

> In the case of analytic inference we know the probability of our conclusion (if the premisses are true), but in the case of synthetic inferences we only know the degree of trustworthiness of our proceeding.[48]

> The validity of induction consists in the fact that it proceeds according to a method which though it may give provisional results that are incorrect will yet, if steadily pursued, eventually correct any such error.[49]

Thus quantitative inductions are not, in Peirce's view, *vindicated,* as Ayer and Madden say, because there is no initial ratio to match as there is in a probable deduction; Don Koehn's view that as early as the *Popular Science Monthly* series Peirce searched for a *sense* in which induction was valid seems right:[50] that sense being that the method, the correct sampling procedure given the proper conditions, would eventually hit upon the true answer, the true answer being seen as the ratio represented in the final interpretant. Suppose we do *not* include and emphasize the inductive *procedure* in our understanding of what quantitative induction is. In this case, Peirce would probably admit that quantitative induction was *not valid* in any sense and revert to his thought of 1867: "What an absurdity it is after all to speak of an ampliative inference."[51]

In the case of theorematic and corollarial deductions it is observed that, if so and so were the case, then such and such, not involving probability, would obtain. In the case of a probable deduction proper, it is observed that, if the population is known to have such and such a distribution of characters, then were the correct sampling procedure to continue, this value would be hit upon and thus, as a prediction, vindicated in the long run. In the case of a quantitative induction, it is observed that, if so and so were the case, where this so and so is thought of as the correct sampling procedure as applied to any population, regular or irregular in its marks, then these marks would be zeroed in on eventually in conformity with the law of large numbers as it appears in the central limit theorem. And it is the discovery of these marks or the approaching of these marks which answers the original question put to nature in every quantitative induction.

Those inferences which Peirce earlier classified as quantitative retroductions but which he later threw in with inductions would best, now, be classified as quantitative inductions. The sort of question put to nature would be this: which sets of marks (such as the marks of barrel #2 or barrel #3, above) are most resembled by the marks of the sample taken. Since a numerical answer can be given to this question, it is a quantitative inference and is best classified as a quantitative induction, even though it is not a paradigmatic case of quantitative induction.

(2) *Qualitative Inductions.* Those inferences which Peirce earlier classified as qualitative retroductions but which he later threw in with inductions would best, now, be classified as qualitative inductions. The sort of question put to nature would be this: which set of marks, such as the marks (qualities) of a number of known chemical substances, are most resembled by the marks (qualitative) of the unknown substance at hand. Not only are such inferences best, now, thrown in with qualitative inductions, but they are among the strongest cases of qualitative inductions. Colorimetric estimates of the amount of a given substance contained in an unknown serve as good examples of qualitative inductions of this variety. Suppose a test tube of water contains an unknown quantity of phosphate and I wish to estimate approximately how much phosphate it contains. I hook up with each of the phosphate radicals an indicator such that the contents of the test tube now turn a certain shade of blue. By using the naked eye and a disc colorimeter to compare this shade of blue with the shades of blue of known concentrations of phosphates, I can estimate the amount of phosphate in the unknown.

A typical example of a qualitative induction begins by asking of nature some such question as this: are the remains of animals left in more recent geological strata the remains of more advanced species or less advanced species? With this question in mind and with at least a rough idea of which species are more advanced, the geological strata can be sampled to obtain an estimate of what the answer is. Qualitative inductions take place, Peirce wrote, after a reasoner already holds an hypothesis more or less problematically.[52]

We may problematically hold the hypothesis that light is a stream of photons: we figure that *whatever* phenomenon involving light should happen to be considered in our future experiments, this phenomenon would probably be accounted for by this hypothesis. Of course, the kind of probability involved in this case of a qualitative induction is neither *a priori* probability nor *frequency* probability, but probability in the sense of *reasonability*. From the point of view of semiotics, the premisses of the qualitative induction serve as a sign of the conclusion, but the strength of the argument is weak relative to the strength of quantitative induction. We have a so-far-so-good attitude toward our best hypotheses; we take it that whatever weight we give to the supposition that they are true is qualitative, and we take it that it would be fruitless, given our present state of knowledge of the universe, to try in any Carnapian or Popperian way to reduce these to ratios.

Qualitative inductions include very crude inferences, such as the inference that since seminary philosophers have usually reasoned badly they shall continue to reason badly; or the inference that since no instance of clairvoyance has yet been established, there probably is no such thing.[53] (Here, the term *probability* is taken to mean reasonability or, at best, likelihood; not *a priori* or *a posteriori* quantitative probability). Crude inductions are often sufficiently weak to become fallacies. In any case Peirce called some kinds of very crude qualitative inductions "pooh pooh" arguments.[54]

It is an important feature of Peirce's system of logic to notice that as one proceeds down the spectrum of qualitative inductions from the stronger to the weaker varieties, the amount of side argumentation, the amount of supplementary information, and the number of presuppositions required to make the inductions plausible gradually increases. Somewhere along this spectrum the transition occurs between critical logic and transuasional logic or speculative rhetoric.[55]

I earlier described the sixth natural class of inferences, abductions (1133). Peirce emphasized the rhematic character of abduction in the following passage:

An originary argument, or *abduction*, is an argument which presents
facts in its Premiss which present a similarity to the fact stated in the
Conclusion, but which could perfectly well be true without the latter
being so, much more without its being recognized; so that we are not led
to assert the Conclusion positively but are only inclined toward admit-
ting it as representing a fact of which the facts of the Premiss constitute
an *Icon*. . . . An Abduction is Originary in respect to being the only kind
of argument which starts a new idea.[56]

Peirce gave the classical example of how the resemblance between the
locus of an ellipse and the observed positions of Mars led Kepler to
adopt the hypothesis that Mars moved in an ellipse.[57]

At one point Peirce defined critical logic as "the science of what is
quasi-necessarily true of the *representamina* of any scientific intelligence in
order that they may hold good of any *object*, that is, may be true."[58]
This definition suggested that the weaker forms of inference do properly belong in obsistent logic by virtue of being *quasi-necessary*. As the
transition to transuasional logic and to transuasive arguments takes
place, attention switches away from the normative question of the
strengths of various kinds of inferences and toward the question of
what the probable course of nature is. Here, as we shall see, presuppositions are used extensively and weak arguments (degenerate forms of
deduction) are interpreted as stronger arguments than they would be
without these presuppositions. Peirce alluded to the transition from
weak arguments to transuasional logic in the following passage.

Of what use does this new logical doctrine promise to be? The first
service it may be expected to render is that of correcting a considerable
number of hasty assumptions about logic which have been allowed to
affect philosophy. In the next place, if Kant has shown that metaphysical conceptions spring from formal logic, this great generalisation upon
formal logic must lead to a new apprehension of the metaphysical conceptions which shall render them more adequate to the needs of science.
In short, "exact" logic will prove a stepping-stone to "exact" metaphysics. In the next place, it must immensely widen our logical notions. For
example, a class consisting of a lot of things jumbled higgledy-piggledy
must now be seen to be but a degenerate form of the more general idea
of a *system*. Generalisation, which has hitherto meant passing to a larger
class, must mean taking in the conception of the whole system of which
we see but a fragment, etc., etc. In the next place, it is already evident to
those who know what has already been made out, that that speculative
rhetoric, or objective logic, mentioned at the beginning of this article, is
destined to grow into a colossal doctrine which may be expected to lead
to most important philosophical conclusions.[59]

VI

SPECULATIVE RHETORIC (1)

The system of signs described in originalian logic is a system of possibilities. The system of arguments described in obsistent logic is a classification of arguments according to the strength of each, and this strength is essentially a function of obsistencies. The culminating member of the triad of logics is *transuasional logic* or *speculative rhetoric*. Here we turn to persuasive arguments as to which possibilities are actualized in the world; and at the center of attention in transuasional logic are the *probable* ways of nature, not in the sense of ratio but in the sense of what is likely or what might reasonably be expected, all things considered.[1]

The terms Peirce used for his triad of logics parallel Roman terms for three of the seven liberal arts: grammar, logic, and rhetoric.[2] Peirce used the term *speculative* in the sense in which Scotus used *speculativa*, so that *speculative rhetoric* and *speculative grammar* should be thought of as *theoretical* or *pure* sciences.[3] Peirce said that the task of pure rhetoric was "to ascertain the laws by which in every scientific intelligence one sign gives birth to another, and especially one thought brings forth another."[4] Aristotle defined *rhetoric* as "the faculty of observing in any given case the available means of persuasion."[5] One of the central themes of Aristotle's *Rhetoric* is that in order to persuade ordinary people to do ordinary things (such as to defend their country), *reason* should be used but *not* demonstrative arguments. Ordinary people do not take to demonstrative arguments, especially systems of syllogisms complete with self-evident first principles. Aristotle recommended the use of arguments which are easily understood, even if weak, such as analogies, arguments from signs, likelihoods, and arguments employing popular maxims such as the argument that no man is free because every man is the slave of money or fortune. Aristotle wrote that *enthymemes* are the substance of rhetoric.[6] It is not clear how Aristotle used

the term *enthymeme,* but it seems to have been a covering term for a
variety of weak argument forms. While contemporary logicians think
of enthymemes as incomplete arguments, especially incomplete syllogisms, Aristotle thought of enthymemes in a wider sense as including
weak but marketable arguments. In the *Century Dictionary* Peirce said
that Aristotle included arguments from signs and likelihoods within the
compass of enthymemes.[7] *Speculative rhetoric* will also use weak but marketable argument forms in an effort to persuade the listener that the
ways of nature are probably such and such.

Transuasional logic, as the culminating member of the triad of logics,
is methodeutic proper.[8] Transuasional logic may be understood as induction, the third stage of inquiry, if induction is taken to mean especially arguments put forward in support of hypotheses concerning this
world.[9] A *transuasive argument* considers, on the one hand, possibilities
such as those suggested by originalian logic, and, on the other hand,
the conditions set in obsistent logic as to what constitutes a strong
argument. In this respect, transuasional logic mediates between originalian logic and obsistent logic. Transuasional arguments themselves
are essentially weak argument forms, such as qualitative inductions,
which are interpreted as being stronger arguments than they are by
presupposing additional premisses, much after the manner of Mill's suggestion that an inductive argument, though itself weak, becomes a
strong argument (approximating a deduction) by adding a major premiss to the effect that nature is uniform. Given sufficiently strong
presuppositions, a multitude of otherwise weak inferences are readily
understood to be rational and strong. For example, in a controlled
experiment such as keeping the pressure of a gas constant while observing the effect of temperature changes upon volume, we may suppose there are no other possible causes for the observed changes in
volume. By supposing that every event is the effect of one and only one
cause, together with a few other suppositions, all of Mill's methods of
experimental inquiry may be reduced to variations of the disjunctive
syllogism since the method of residues may be understood as indicating
that such and such a cause may not be eliminated and all the other
methods as showing that such and such a cause may or may not be
eliminated.

Peirce said that the idea that "we ought to experiment without pre-
conceived ideas is one of those vague logical maxims which character-
izes the loose reasoner,"[10] and he made it quite clear that when we

come to the transuasional task of arguing that the ways of nature are such and such, we have no choice other than to make certain presuppositions. Or, perhaps the point should be put this way: when we reason about the probable course of nature we *do not suppress premises* which tend to increase the strength of our argument but rather make a point of incorporating into our argument premises which, while recognized as presuppositions, form an integral part of the transuasive argument. Putting this point in semiotic terms, Peirce said, "A Genuine Sign is a Transuasional Sign, or *Symbol,* which is a sign which owes its significant virtue to a character which can only be realized by the aid of its Interpretant."[11] It should be further noted that, as Peirce insisted, there is in a sense no such thing as a *suppressed premiss:* if a premiss is neither expressed in thought (implicitly or explicitly) nor occurs as part of the leading principle of an argument, then it ceases to be a premiss in any sense and the argument before us is not the same argument it would have been had it included this as a premiss.[12]

We have said that Peirce referred to the guessing instinct as the sheet anchor of science and that he was generally disposed to give due weight to man's natural logicality or *logica utens.* Suppose a man thinks the molecules of a gas bounce around like little rubber balls: Peirce would bet by virtue of the circumstances that this possibility seems plausible to that man, that the man's idea is worth something.[13] Archimedes thought that the effect of putting two weights alongside each other in a balance pan would have the same effect as if they have been stacked one on top of the other, and this idea has worked out fairly well in mechanics.[14] It is natural for a man to attend to the uniformities or regularities in the world and to form his expectations accordingly. The thinking of the average, enthusiastic gambler well illustrates this tendency. Suppose such a gambler steps up to play roulette and to bet on either red or black. Suppose he watches the game for a short time and observes that the ball falls on black four times in a row. And suppose the gambler now confidently bets that black will come up again on the fifth turn of the wheel. *Qua* reasoning, such a bet is often criticized on the basis of the following considerations. In cases where we know *a priori* all the possibilities involved relative to a certain kind of event, we list these and define the probability of an event as the ratio of favorable cases to total number of cases. Setting aside the fact that roulette wheels always have zeros and double zeros, there are two possible outcomes for a given spin of the wheel and the probability of getting black is one-half. This *a priori* probability remains the same regardless of the character of the preceding series. After a run of four blacks, then, it is considered to be *the gambler's fallacy* either if the gambler bets confidently on black, thinking that what has been happening will continue to happen, or if he bets confidently on red, thinking red is about due. These confident bets are considered unwarranted on the *a priori* grounds that a series of four blacks and one red is equi-possible in two respects with a series of five blacks: (1) considering the fifth turn in itself as an independent event, the probability of black is one-half; and (2) when we construct a list of all possible outcomes for five turns the sequence of five blacks appears on that list exactly once, and so does the sequence of four blacks and one red. However, relative to his premises, in neither the case where the gambler confidently bets on black nor the case where he confidently bets on red is there a mistaken inference or a gambler's fallacy in *that sense*. At one time a gambler will focus his attention upon or be aware of one regularity and at another time of a different regularity. When he attends to the regularity that blacks and all blacks are coming up, he bets on black. When he attends to the regularity that blacks and reds come up with about equal frequency and that the present sequence is, from that point of view, due to change, he bets on *that* regularity. What is eminently reasonable is to think that past regularities will continue and this is exactly what the unsophisticated gambler does. A more sophisticated gambler reasons in the same basic way, differing only in that he is aware of more information and attends to different regularities.

Whatever presuppositions are involved in transuasive arguments are essentially no more than possibilities, as much as we may be inclined to accept them. The history of philosophy shows that philosophers almost invariably make the mistake of taking whatever they are inclined to think to actually be true. Examples of this "method," which Peirce called the "philosopher's method" or the "method of inclination,"[15] would be the following: to claim that the intervals between the planets are harmonic intervals because there is a music of the spheres; to claim that the motion of the stars is noble because they are close to the unmoved mover; to claim that the motion of the stars is circular because that motion is noble. What has been called the "balancing of reasons" sounds like reasoning, but what is placed in each pan?[16] Nothing more than an inclination, so that this, again, is the philosopher's method. The philosopher's "method" is to base apparent results on *desultory* experience as opposed to systematic investigation.[17] Thus, their base is weaker than it pretends to be and their result is pretended to be stronger than it is. Hegel is a good example of one who used the philosopher's method. Concerning Hegel, Peirce wrote:

> He recognizes clearly what he is about. He simply launches his boat into the current of thought and allows himself to be carried wherever the current leads. He himself calls his method *dialectic,* meaning that a frank discussion of the difficulties to which any opinion spontaneously gives rise will lead to modification after modification until a tenable position is attained. This is a distinct profession of faith in the method of inclinations.[18]

Whatever *presuppositions* are involved in a transuasive argument as to what might be possible in nature cannot really be, or have originated from, a list of pure logical possibilities. In game models of probability, we first set up lists of possibilities and go on to calculate probabilities. But we have no *a priori* list of what hypotheses are logically possible. Relative to certain universes of discourse we can start off to construct a list of pure logical possibilities, but unless we know what to count as significant possibilities such a list quickly expands and becomes useless. For example, how many arrangements are there of eight elements and their complements? Would the possibilities include combinations? Permutations? Distributions? Sets which are complements of other sets which are complements? Spatial arrangements, so that the elements of any of these sets might form a cube or a dodecahedron or a prism? Purely logical possibilities, Peirce wrote, "vary and diverge from one another . . . in every possible way" so that in effect "there is no anatomy of [pure] possibilities."[19]

We must make some presuppositions and if these cannot be pure logical possibilities, they must be real possibilities, that is, those consistent with originalian logic, obsistent logic, and careful investigations of the empirical world. The overall strength of any transuasive argument is a function of how carefully its presuppositions are thought out and of the extent to which these are based on empirical observations.

Consider, for example, the presupposition that nature is uniform. This is perhaps the most commonly used presupposition in science and yet it is not generally recognized as a mere possibility, it is not well thought out, and it is not based upon careful observations of the real world. There are a multitude of senses of *uniformity:* the members of a collection might resemble each other most closely, as one piece of gold resembles another; a quality may tend to run through every member of a collection, as the quality of having mass; certain characteristics may tend to cluster into groups, such as those of maturing slowly and living longer; and a thing may tend to possess all of a set of characteristics if it possesses any, for example, a man who believes the Pope is infallible is likely to believe in other doctrines of Christianity as well.[20] Those who presuppose that *nature is uniform* do not usually say in what sense they think this is true, and they seldom back up their claim with reference to the ways of observed *phenomena*. Peirce was a careful observer. It seemed to him that the number of irregularities in the world outnumbered the number of regularities, though of course no definite numbers could be assigned to either. We are naturally inclined to attend to the regularities, he said, and to take an interest in irregularities only when these are seen as breaks in some regularity.[21]

The transuasional logician takes risks.[22] Amidst his rhetoric as to the ways of the universe, he may presuppose, for example, that the universe will continue to exist, that the conditions will be such that induction will work, that even if the universe is infinite our samples might nevertheless represent this infinite population in some way, as, for example, would be the case if the kind of infinity involved were like the infinity of a repeating decimal.[23] At one point Peirce said that the presuppositions of logic are merely hopes;[24] but this in no way releases the inquirer from his duty to use only well-considered presuppositions.

The most important presupposition Peirce used is the presupposition that the world is everywhere continuous. It would be a prize-winning error to take Peirce's idea of continuity to be equivalent to the idea that nature is uniform, because the idea of continuity includes firsts, seconds, and thirds, unlike any nominalism. Peirce's presupposition of continuity is certainly well thought out and well supported by evidence—relative to any other great presuppositions. Peirce thought of this presupposition of continuity as clearly in line with nineteenth-century thought:

> Endeavors to effectuate continuity have been the great task of the Nineteenth Century. To bind together ideas, to bind together facts, to bind together knowledge, to bind together sentiment, to bind together the purposes of men, to bind together industry, to bind together great works, to bind together power, to bind together nations into great natural, living, and enduring systems was the business that lay before our great grandfathers to commence and which we now see just about to pass into a second and more advanced stage of achievement. Such a

work will not be aided by regarding continuity as an unreal figment, it cannot but be helped by regarding it as the really possible eternal order of things to which we are trying to make our arbitrariness conform.

As to detached ideas, they are of value only so far as, directly or indirectly, they can be made conducive to the development of systems of ideas. There is no such thing as an absolutely detached idea. It would be no idea at all. For an idea is itself a continuous system. But of ideas those are most suggestive which detached though they seem are in fact fragments broken from great systems.[25]

Peirce used the term *synechism* to refer to the presupposition that the world is a continuum. Max Fisch expressed the opinion that in all that Peirce wrote on continuity the key sentence is, "Synechism is not an ultimate and absolute metaphysical doctrine: It is a regulative principle of logic, prescribing what sort of hypothesis is fit to be entertained."[26] It is conceivable that a scientist might be making use of the presupposition that everything in nature is part of a system without making a point of it; if so, he is using what Peirce calls *indagation* or the silent method of science.[27] Since continuity is the parent of the entire system of our *logica utens*, it may be that indagation is the silent extrapolation of phaneroscopy.

Transuasional logic or speculative rhetoric is also called, by Peirce, *objective logic*.[28] In calling it objective logic, Peirce had in mind the great systems of *Naturphilosophie* of such men as Schelling and Hegel. Peirce described his philosophy as a "Schelling-fashioned idealism"[29] and, in an often quoted passage, said:

> The one intelligible theory of the universe is that of objective idealism, that matter is effete mind, inveterate habits becoming physical laws. But before this can be accepted it must show itself capable of explaining the tridimensionality of space, the laws of motion, and the general characteristics of the universe, with mathematical clearness and precision; for no less should be demanded of every philosophy.[30]

Peirce, in looking over Hegel's account of the development of the Absolute Spirit, cannot believe that Hegel includes thirds but completely omits seconds and firsts. Hegel pretends to be tracing the development of ideas as they work themselves out and become what they are, but he leaves no room for chance or necessity. Peirce called Hegel's logic a *Keely Motor*, meaning that it does not work.[31] Hegel's metaphysics, like Kant's, suffered from his lack of knowledge of logic. In comparing his own philosophy with Hegel's, Peirce wrote:

Now the question arises, what necessarily resulted from that state of things? But the only sane answer is that where freedom was boundless nothing in particular necessarily resulted.

In this proposition lies the prime difference between my objective logic and that of Hegel. He says, if there is any sense in philosophy at all, the whole universe and every feature of it, however minute, is rational, and was constrained to be as it is by the logic of events, so that there is no principle of action in the universe but reason. But I reply, this line of thought, though it begins rightly, is not exact. A logical slip is committed; and the conclusion reached is manifestly at variance with observation. It is true that the whole universe and every feature of it must be regarded as rational, that is as brought about by the logic of events. But it does not follow that it is *constrained* to be as it is by the logic of events; for the logic of evolution and of life need not be supposed to be of that wooden kind that absolutely constrains a given conclusion. The logic may be that of the inductive or hypothetic inference.

This may-be is at once converted into must-be when we reflect that among the facts to be accounted for are such as that, for example, red things look red and not blue and *vice versa*. It is obvious that that cannot be a necessary consequence of abstract being.

The effect of this error of Hegel is that he is forced to deny [the] fundamental character of two elements of experience which cannot result from deductive logic. What these elements are will appear in the sequel.[32]

Peirce's theory of scientific discovery culminates in speculative rhetoric, the last of the three departments of his system of logic and the stronghold of the idea that the system of nature is identical with the system of thought. As a *philosophy* (as opposed to a system of logic) this is objective idealism. Peirce respected objective idealism as a type of philosophy, because he felt it honestly addressed itself to *the problem of philosophy:* that problem being to show "what can be found . . . intelligible and reasonable in the universe at large."[33] From the point of view of the theory of discovery, if it be the case that the system of nature and the system of thought are parts of one system, this benefits us in at least three ways: (1) to know the natural classes of ideas is to know the kinds of hypotheses concerning nature which are worth pursuing; (2) in cases where these hypotheses are accepted, we at one and the same time know the ways of nature and know these intuitively; and (3) if such natural hypotheses work better than counter-intuitive hypotheses, there is hope that our system of logic will be complete because in that case there would be no room left for anything which is purportedly incognizable, unintelligible, or mysterious.

Peirce at times put his general perspective (both philosophical and logical) in somewhat poetic terms—though not in original poetic terms. We can look at ourselves as having an essence which mirrors the essence of physical reality and which by virtue of this circumstance may be used to get at the essence of physical reality (especially the unseen). Peirce borrowed the phrase "man's glassy essence" from Shakespeare's *Measure for Measure:*[34]

> Man, proud man, dressed in a little brief authority.
> Most ignorant of what he's most assured,
> His glassy essence.

VII

SPECULATIVE RHETORIC (2)

In this chapter I give a brief account of Peirce's *classification* of the sciences. He envisaged the sciences as forming a system of *natural* classes running from mathematics down to the special descriptive sciences.

Peirce wrote that in beginning the task of classifying the sciences, the first question to ask is this: what is meant by a natural class?[1] We already know something about natural classes—the natural classes of ideas are all offspring of the most general, most indeterminate idea of thirdness. Peirce believed that the idea of continuity had a great office to fulfill in all *natural* classifications and that all *natural* classes were necessarily indeterminate.[2] In order to clarify the meaning of *natural* class Peirce recommended that we turn to the *naturalists*. It is the naturalists who are the great builders of conceptions, Peirce observed, and "we must, in great measure, take them for our teachers in this important part of logic."[3]

Peirce found that the naturalists build *their* conceptions by utilizing the idea of passing "from one form to another by insensible degrees."[4] The following passage will give the reader an idea of what Peirce had in mind:

> When a naturalist wishes to study a species, he collects a considerable number of specimens more or less similar. In contemplating them, he observes certain ones which are more or less alike in some particular respect. They all have, for instance, a certain *S*-shaped marking. He observes that they are not *precisely* alike, in this respect; the *S* has not precisely the same shape, but the differences are such as to lead him to believe that forms could be found intermediate between any two of those he possesses. He, now, finds other forms apparently quite dissimilar—say a marking in the form of a *C*—and the question is, whether he can find intermediate ones which will connect these latter with the others. This he often succeeds in doing in cases where it would at first be thought impos-

sible; whereas, he sometimes finds those which differ, at first glance, much less, to be separated in Nature by the non-occurrence of intermediaries. In this way, he builds up from the study of Nature a new general conception of the character in question. He obtains, for example, an idea of a leaf which includes every part of the flower, and an idea of a vertebra which includes the skull. I surely need not say much to show what a logical engine is here. It is the essence of the method of the naturalist.[5]

Max Fisch remarks that during the Arisbe period Peirce found the reasoning of Agassiz more cogent than that of the evolutionists.[6] In reference to Agassiz, Peirce wrote "I will just set down his vague definitions and allow myself to be vaguely influenced by them."[7]

After a careful study of a number of ways of classifying animals, Agassiz adopted with only minor changes the following system of Cuvier:[8]

Branch I: Vertebrata
    Class I: Mammalia
        Order I: Bimana
    Class II: Birds
    Class III: Reptiles
    Class IV: Fishes

Branch II: Mollusca
    Class I: Cephalopoda
    Class II: Pteropoda
    Class III: Gastropoda
    Class IV: Acephala
    Class V: Brachiopoda
    Class VI: Cirrhopoda

Branch III: Articulata
    Class I: Annelides
    Class II: Crustacea
    Class III: Arachnides
    Class IV: Insects

Branch IV: Radiata
    Class I: Echinoderms
    Class II: Intestinal worms
    Class III: Acalephae
    Class IV: Polypi
    Class V: Infusoria

According to Agassiz, naturalists were fairly confident that there was something to the divisions they called species, but not confident there was anything to any of the other so-called natural divisions.[9] It was in vogue in Agassiz's day to believe that the physical environment in which an animal lived determined the nature of the animal.[10] Agassiz, one of the few naturalists who disagreed with the Darwinian view, thought that since the same kinds of animals existed in different environments and since different kinds existed in the same environment, there was no simple correspondence between environment and type;[11] not that the environment did not influence an individual, but that the environment did not determine kinds of individuals. In Agassiz's opinion each animal exhibited a general plan upon which it had been built and there were also different ways in which a given plan might be carried out. Agassiz believed that branches, classes, and orders, along with species, were in some sense real.[12] He believed that these were divine conceptions and that there was in fact a divine plan whether or not any naturalist had as yet figured out what that plan was.[13] According to Agassiz, the different classification schemes of the different naturalists were successive approximations to God's plan and to His ways of carrying out the plan. That naturalists were getting closer and closer to discovering this plan (they are getting closer and closer in Agassiz's view) indicates that our intellect and the divine intellect must be identical or at least very similar.[14] The following shows Agassiz's religious sentiment in the matter:

> All these facts in their natural connection proclaim aloud the One God, whom man may know, adore, and love; and Natural History must in good time become the analysis of the thoughts of the Creator of the Universe, as manifested in the animal and vegetable kingdoms, as well as in the inorganic world.[15]

> I disclaim every intention of introducing in this work any evidence irrelevant to my subject or of supporting any conclusions not immediately flowing from it; but I cannot overlook nor disregard here the close connection there is between the facts ascertained by scientific investigations and the discussions now carried on respecting the origin of organized beings. And though I know those who hold it to be very unscientific to believe that thinking is not something inherent in matter, and that there is an essential difference between inorganic and living and thinking beings, I shall not be prevented by any such pretensions of a false philosophy from expressing my conviction that as long as it cannot be shown that matter or physical forces do actually reason, I shall consider any manifestation of thought as evidence of the existence of a thinking being as the author of such thought, and shall look upon an intelligent

and intelligible connection between the facts of nature as direct proof of the existence of a thinking God, as certainly as man exhibits the power of thinking when he recognizes their natural relations.[16]

And when, in our pride of philosophy, we thought that we were inventing systems of science and classifying creation by the force of our own reason, have we followed only, and reproduced, in our imperfect expressions, the plan whose foundations were laid in the dawn of creation, and the development of which we are laboriously studying—thinking, as we put together and arrange our fragmentary knowledge, that we are introducing order into chaos anew? Is this order the result of the exertions of human skill and ingenuity, or is it inherent in the objects themselves, so that the intelligent student of Natural History is led unconsciously, by the study of the animal kingdom itself, to these conclusions, the great divisions under which he arranges animals being indeed but the headings to the chapters of the great book which he is reading? To me it appears indisputable that this order and arrangement of our studies are based upon the natural, primitive relations of animal life—those systems to which we have given the names of the great leaders of our science who first proposed them being in truth but translations into human language of the thoughts of the Creator. And if this is indeed so, do we not find in this adaptability of the human intellect to the facts of creation, by which we become instinctively, and as I have said, unconsciously, the translators of the thoughts of God, the most conclusive proof of our affinity with the Divine Mind? And is not this intellectual and spiritual connection with the Almighty worthy of our deepest consideration? If there is any truth in the belief that man is made in the image of God, it is surely not amiss for the philosopher to endeavor, by the study of his own mental operations, to approximate the workings of the Divine Reason, learning from the nature of his own mind better to understand the Infinite Intellect from which it is derived. Such a suggestion may at first sight appear irreverent. But who is the truly humble? He who, penetrating into the secrets of creation, arranges them under a formula which he proudly calls his scientific system? Or he who, in the same pursuit, recognizes his glorious affinity with the Creator, and in deepest gratitude for so sublime a birthright strives to be the faithful interpreter of that Divine Intellect with whom he is permitted, nay, with whom he is intended, according to the laws of his being, to enter into communion?[17]

Agassiz thought that in principle the *branches* of a classificatory scheme should attempt to get at whatever distinctly different plans were being followed, the *classes* should attempt to get at the different manners in which the plan of a branch was being carried out, the *orders* should attempt to get at the proper ranking of members of a class

according to some principle such as the level of complexity of a structure, and that *families* were simply what first strikes the eye of the
naturalist, the readily spotted groups of animals such as the humming-
birds, for example.

Peirce said he tried about a hundred different ways of classifying the
sciences (this over a period of forty years).[18] By 1903 he more or less
settled down to the following classification of the sciences:[19]

> Branch I: Pure Sciences or Sciences of Discovery
>   Class I: Mathematical Sciences
>   Order I: Mathematics of Logic
>   Order II: Mathematics of Discrete Series
>   Order III: Mathematics of Continua or Pseudo-Continua
>   Class II: Cenoscopic Sciences
>   Order I: Phaneroscopy
>   Order II: Normative Sciences (Esthetics, Ethics, Logic [Semi-
>   otic])
>   Order III: Metaphysics
>   Class III: Idioscopic Sciences
>   Order I: Nomological Sciences of Mind and of Matter
>   Order II: Classificatory Sciences of Mind and of Matter
>   Order III: Descriptive Sciences of Mind and of Matter
>
> Branch II: Sciences of Review
>
> Branch III: Practical Sciences and Technology

Branches, Classes and *Orders* are all natural classes. Peirce described a
natural class as follows:

> So then, a natural class being a family whose members are the sole
> offspring and vehicles of one idea, from which they derive their peculiar
> faculty, to classify by abstract definitions is simply a sure means of avoid-
> ing a natural classification. . . . When one can lay one's finger upon the
> purpose to which a class of things owes its origin, then indeed abstract
> definition may formulate that purpose. But when one cannot do that,
> but one can trace the genesis of a class and ascertain how several have
> been derived by different lines of descent from one less specialized
> form, this is the best route toward an understanding of what the natural
> classes are. This is true even in biology; it is more clearly so when the
> objects generated are, like sciences, themselves of the nature of ideas.[20]

> There are cases where we are quite in the dark, alike concerning the
> creating purpose and concerning the genesis of things; but [there are
> cases] where we find a system of classes connected with a system of

abstract ideas—most frequently numbers—and that in such a manner as to give us reason to guess that those ideas in some way, usually obscure, determine the possibilities of the things. For example, chemical compounds, generally—or at least the more decidedly characterized of them, including, it would seem, the so-called elements—seem to belong to types, so that, to take a single example, chlorates $KClO_3$, manganates $KMnO_3$, bromates $KBrO_3$, rutheniates $KRuO_3$, iodates KIO_3, behave chemically in strikingly analogous ways. That this sort of argument for the existence of natural classes—I mean the argument drawn from types, that is, from a connection between the things and a system of formal ideas—may be stronger and more direct than one might expect to find it, is shown by the circumstances that ideas themselves—and are they not the easiest of all things to classify naturally, with assured truth?—can be classified on no other grounds than this, except in a few exceptional cases. Even in these few cases, this method would seem to be the safest. For example, in pure mathematics, almost all the classification reposes on the relations of the forms classified to numbers or other multitudes. Thus, in topical geometry, figures are classified according to the whole numbers attached to their *choresis, cyclosis, periphraxis, apeiresis,* etc. As for the exceptions such as the classes of hessians, jacobians, invariants, vectors, etc., they all depend upon types, too, although upon types of a different kind. It is plain that it must be so; and all the natural classes of logic will be found to have the same character.[21]

Branch I includes the *pure sciences* or the *sciences of discovery.* Being a *branch,* it ought to make reference to a goal or purpose as Agassiz had suggested.[22] It was Peirce's opinion that the sciences of discovery did have a goal and that was to *understand* the universe. Putting this opinion in more poetic, more idealistic, and perhaps more accurate terms, Peirce wrote:

Consider, for a moment, what Reason, as well as we can today conceive it, really is. . . . The very being of the General, of Reason, *consists* in its governing individual events. . . . It is like the character of a man which consists in the ideas that he will conceive and in the effort that he will make, and which only develops as the occasions actually arise. . . . The one thing whose admirableness is not due to an ulterior reason is Reason itself comprehended in all its fullness, so far as we can comprehend it. Under this conception, the ideal of conduct will be to execute our little function in the operation of the creation by giving a hand toward rendering the world more reasonable whenever, as the slang is, it is "up to us" to do so. In logic, it will be observed that knowledge is reasonableness; and the ideal of reasoning will be to follow such methods as must develop knowledge the most speedily.[23]

Class I (the mathematical sciences), *Class II* (the cenoscopic sciences), and *Class III* (the idioscopic sciences) were arrived at as the three classes of the sciences of discovery by giving a great deal of weight to the relation between the sciences and the natural classes of ideas[24] and less weight to other factors relevant to the classification of the sciences, such as the historical classes of sciences to which Peirce referred as the categories of the course of research.[25] As natural classes, mathematics, cenoscopy, and idioscopy fall within the natural class of *argument* symbolic legisign because mathematics, cenoscopy, and idioscopy all reason about the laws of their respective domains and interpret these laws as legisigns. Mathematics differs from cenoscopy and idioscopy because the possibilities about which it reasons are not limited to the field of possibilities which may apply to the real world. Cenoscopy differs from idioscopy in that it reasons about the more common and easily accessible aspects of experience—those more or less readily available to all of us without need of special equipment or resources. Peirce envisaged the three classes as forming a system with movement, interchanges and connections running in all directions. At the same time, certain kinds of connections run essentially in one direction. For example, the idioscopic sciences do depend upon mathematics for results, whereas mathematics can get along without the results obtained in the special sciences. For instance, the brightness of phenomenal light varies as the *logarithm* of the intensity of that light: this relationship could not be accurately observed without reference to the *logarithm function* or an equivalent function. The intensity of that light varies as the *antilogarithm* of the brightness of the phenomenal light: this relationship could not be accurately observed without reference to the *antilogarithm function* or an equivalent function. Both functions are better understood with reference to *inverse functions* and then on to the *general idea of a function*. The idea of a function, on the other hand, may be obtained without reference to the relationship between the brightness of phenomenal light and the intensity of phenomenal light. While idioscopic observations are, of necessity, set within the cenoscopic field (that is, within the context of the ordinary world and our common-sense understanding of things) they do not, at present, depend upon any *results* obtained in cenoscopy. As we have suggested, Peirce hoped this would change as we do come to get some results in cenoscopy. At one point (in speaking about the lowest order of cenoscopy, metaphysics), Peirce said that, even more than the rest of cenoscopy, metaphysics was a "puny, rickety and scrofulous science."[26] At another point, he said it would be a great thing if the uncertainties of metaphysics could be reduced to a mere hundred times the uncertainties of astronomy or chemistry.[27]

Each class of the sciences of discovery has its *orders*.[28] The *highest order of mathematics, the mathematics of logic,* will draw necessary conclusions concerning the most general mathematical conceptions and these will be depended upon by the lower orders of mathematics. For example, the idea of a group is higher than the idea of an algebraic system. The *highest order of cenoscopy, phaneroscopy,* will work at discovering natural classes of ideas. These seem to be a function of certain limitations placed upon the field of thought, as we have seen. The lower orders of cenoscopy are the normative sciences and metaphysics. The normative sciences include esthetics, controlled ethical actions, and the controlled inferences of Peirce's system of logic. Metaphysics studies things like space and time. But we cannot *think of* what might be of value in itself or *think of* actions controlled so as to reach some goal or of classes of inferences or of space or time except within the field of what kinds of thoughts it is *possible* for us *to think.* The *orders of idioscopy* are so arranged as to put investigations of the *fundamental laws of nature* in the *first order, nomological psychics* and *physics.* The classificatory and descriptive sciences represent further determinations of the nomological laws of psychics and physics, in line with the order of development of natural classes. While Peirce was a great student of the history of science, he never believed that natural classes of idioscopic sciences would be identified *simply* by tracing their historical genealogies as opposed to tracing their semiotic development. No simply historical genealogy of the sub-divisions of *this branch* of science has the capacity to show their semiotic genesis. Concerning the *genesis* of the sciences, Peirce expressed this opinion:

> Speaking in a broad, rough way, it may be said that the sciences have grown out of the useful arts, or out of arts supposed to be useful. Astronomy out of astrology; physiology, taking medicine as a halfway out of magic; chemistry out of alchemy; thermotics from the steam-engine, etc. Among the theoretical sciences, while some of the most abstract have sprung straight from the concretest arts, there is nevertheless a well-marked tendency for a science to be first descriptive, later classificatory, and lastly to embrace all classes in one law. The classificatory stage may be skipped. Yet in true order of development, the gen-

eration proceeds quite in the other direction. Men may and do begin to study the different kinds of animals and plants before they know anything of the general laws of physiology. But they cannot attain any true understanding of taxonomic biology until they can be guided by the discoveries of the physiologists. Till then the study of mollusks will be nothing but conchology. On the other hand the physiologist may be aided by a fact or two here and there drawn from taxonomic biology; but he asks but little and that little not very urgently of anything that the taxonomist can tell him and that he could not find out for himself.[29]

VIII

SPECULATIVE RHETORIC (3)

If nature and thought are parts of the same system, then it may well be the case that whatever *constraints* apply to the system of thought apply as well to the system of nature. Or, to put it another way, our main goal is to discover whatever constraints obtain on the one system of thought and nature, and if the only way we can observe these constraints on the entire system is by observing the constraints on thought, then that hypothesis is worth pursuing. Originalian logic may be viewed as supplying a map which shows the general constraints upon ideas. Critical logic may be viewed as supplying indications on this map of what condition must obtain in order that some ideas may be considered true. The basic move of speculative rhetoric or transuasional logic is to take this well-prepared map and use it, together with whatever supplementary arguments and general concepts are available from the sciences, as a guide to the ways of nature.

Peirce was fond of emphasizing the fact that men like Galileo and Huygens had taken advantage of their common sense and *il lume naturale* and that it was this which led up to our modern conception of things like *force* and *law*.[1] Kant had learned of the constraints on physical systems from Euler and D'Alembert and applied this idea to thought. Peirce carried out a more accurate survey of thought, a survey which produced a better *map* available for exploring the as yet unknown regions of the universe.

The map is a set of constraints which have been observed to apply to thought. These constraints include: *thirdness,* the open, continuous, and monotonic phaneron, sequences of welded ideas; richly variegated clusterings of ideas replete with spontaneity and freshness (*firstness*); elements of thought determined by bonding constraints, the natural classes of ideas or signs, the illative relations, probabilistic inferences of the natural kind (frequency theory); and the very important constraint of *secondness* (which becomes maximal upon the occasion that we distinguish between an internal and an external world). *The map* might be summarized by saying that in the realm of thought it is *semiotic* action which is dominant.[2] In 1902 Peirce said that "uncertain tendencies, unstable states of equilibrium are conditions *sine qua non* for the manifestation of Mind."[3] Manifestations of mind *obey* certain constraints and nature must, if part of the same system, obey the same constraints. We shall now proceed to illustrate this, our illustrations falling into these five sections: (1) the most general constraint on the laws of nature; (2) the monotonic constraint; (3) constraints on the mind-body interface; (4) constraints on the atom; (5) further constraints on the atom.

Section 1: The most general constraint on the laws of nature. The laws of nature are not necessary in the sense of causal determinism, but the laws of nature are constrained to be signs and, in particular, *argument* symbolic legisigns. In Critical Logic, we found the paradigmatic inference form to be the illative relation, $A \prec B$. The laws of nature obey this constraint, for they are of the form: if so and so were the case, then such and such *would be* the case. For example, the most important law in classical mechanics is Newton's second law, which states that $\vec{F}\Delta t = \Delta \vec{p}$. In semiotic terms, this law is an *argument* of the form: if a force were applied to a particle for a duration of time, Δt then the momentum $(m\vec{v})$ of that particle would change by an amount equal to the product of $\vec{F}$ and Δt. ($F\Delta t$ is called the *impulse*.)

The *concepts* which are involved in laws and the *things* which are involved in laws are parts of one continuous system of ideas and obey the same *would be* constraint. Indeed, concepts and things may be looked upon as mini-laws. In "How to Make Our Ideas Clear," Peirce explained that it was a mistake to think of the concept *force* as mysterious or incognizable because we think of force in a clear way by thinking of the changes in velocities which define force.[4] In connection with this, Peirce gave the famous *pragmatic maxim:* "Consider what effects, which might conceivably have practical bearings, we conceive the object of our conception to have. Then, our conception of these effects is the whole of our conception of the object."[5] The conceivable is what lies within the limitations of the natural classes of signs.

In Peirce's opinion experimentalists right from their medieval beginnings focused their attention upon *would bes* or observable properties of things and not upon anything like material objects or substantial forms. Peirce quoted Petrus Peregrinus (1558) as having written:

> "Inmost of friends! Having been formerly interrogated by thee, I will in a rude narration disclose everywhere the occult nature of the lodestone. For among philosophers nothing is pleasant without participation of knowledge, and the nature of good things is bereaved and clouded in darkness until it is lifted up into the light of mutual surrender. For the love of thee I will write things that to the mob of students are utterly unknown. Nevertheless, of nothing but what is open to observation (*manifestus*) shall we in this letter deliver knowledge, in that this delivery will be part of the treatise in which we shall treat of constructing physical instruments. To treat of the occult properties of this stone concerns the art of sculpturing stone, and though I call the works of which I have inquired open to observation, still they will be inestimable, and to the vulgar they are as illusions and fancies, and therefore in respect to the vulgar they are secret: but to astrologers and naturalists they will be sufficiently open to observation; and to them they will be a solace and for sailing travellers no slight assistance."
>
> [Peirce adds:] We remark that the above passage contains a sort of definition of what was meant by an "occult quality" among the mediaeval physicists. It means a quality not deducible from the Aristotelian doctrine of hot and cold, moist and dry, and not discoverable except by experiment, and therefore a secret to all who do not make experiments, though "satis manifesta" to those who do.[6]

Roscoe (1868) quoted Kirchhoff (1865) as having written—

> "Hence the observations of the solar spectrum appear to me to prove the presence of iron vapour in the solar atmosphere with as great a degree of certainty as we can attain in any question of natural science."
>
> [Roscoe commented:] This statement is, I believe, not one jot more positive than the facts warrant. For what does any evidence in natural science amount to, beyond the expression of a probability? A mineral sent to me from New Zealand is examined by our chemical tests, of which I apply a certain number: and these show me that the mineral contains iron: and no one doubts that my conclusion is correct. Have we, however, in this case, proof positive that the body really is iron? May it not turn out to be a substance which in these respects resembles, but in other respects differs from, the body which we designate as iron? Surely. All we can say is, that in each of the many comparisons which we have made, the properties of the two bodies prove identical, and it is solely this identity of the properties which we express when we call both of them iron.[7]

As another example of a law, consider the chemical equation

$$2NaCl + H_2SO_4 \rightleftarrows 2HCl + Na_2SO_4.[8]$$

Given the appropriate concentrations so that the reaction moves mostly to the right, this means: if sea salt (NaCl) and oil of vitriol (H_2SO_4) were combined in solution, then the result *would be* the spirit of sea salt (HCl) and Glauber's salt (Na_2SO_4). That these chemical elements (Na^+, Cl^-, H^+, and the radical $SO_4^=$) *would*, were they to be together in solution, assume new and favored configurations, is a law. The *would be* (the chemical law) is *real* in the sense that it does make a difference. This *would be* or law does not bring the Na^+, Cl^-, H^+, and $SO_4^=$ into existence, but the existents do obey the law. They move along, as it were, in obedience to the law. The degree of regularity in such chemical reactions is greater than the degree of regularity in phanerochemical reactions, but the difference between the two is itself a matter of degree, not resembling the absolute difference between determinism and freedom. It was Peirce's view that the obedience to law in the case of organic reactions was less regular than in the case of inorganic reactions: he said, for example, that protoplasm, in reacting to chemical changes in its environment, followed laws, but the systems involved were less rigid than those systems involved in the case of crystalline substances.[9]

As another example of a law which obeys semiotic constraints, consider the equation for simple harmonic motion, $x_t = A \sin(\omega t + \varphi_0)$, as this applies to the motion of a simple pendulum. The problem of predicting how a given physical pendulum *would swing* at a given place on the earth's surface with a given force of gravity (g) and a given set of atmospheric conditions within the context of a rotating earth is not an easy problem. Physicists attack the problem by considering a number of closely related but simple situations and problems. So-called *abstract dynamics* is really a zeroing in on a real physical system by considering a sequence of simpler systems, each with constraints which are intuitively clear. Peirce defined a pendulum as "a body so suspended from a fixed point as to move to and fro by the alternate action of gravity and its acquired energy of motion."[10] Peirce defined a simple pendulum as "a material particle suspended by a weightless rod and moving without friction."[11] Consider the diagram of a possible simple pendulum (this diagram is a rhematic iconic *sinsign*).

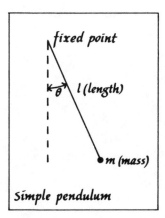

Suppose the mass, *m*, is released at θ and left free to swing back and forth under the force of gravity and without friction. Another rhematic iconic *sinsign* makes clear to us what forces are operating on the mass, *m* (see diagram).

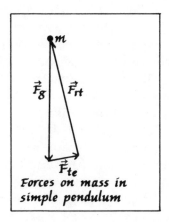

This diagram (a *sinsign*) shows that the force of gravity ($\vec{F}_g$) on *m* is counterbalanced by the radial tension in the rod ($\vec{F}_{rt}$) and the transverse equilibrant ($\vec{F}_{te}$). Since

$$\sin \theta = \vec{F}_{te}/\vec{F}_g$$

$$\vec{F}_{te} = \vec{F}_g \sin \theta$$

and the resultant force $\vec{F}_x$ restoring the pendulum to its equilibrium position is, for a small θ,

$$\vec{F}_x \approx -\vec{F}_g \sin \theta$$

From Newton's law, we have

$$\vec{F}\Delta t = m\Delta\vec{v}$$

where $\vec{F}_x = m(d^2x/dt^2)$

which gives the differential equation

$$m(d^2x/dt^2) + K_x = 0 \qquad \text{where } K = m^g/_l$$

the solution of which is of the form:

$$x_t = A \sin (\omega t + \varphi_0).$$

This "equation of motion" tells us where the pendulum *would be* in its to-and-fro motion after having been released from a given point. The only *idea* in this derivation of the law of motion for the simple pendulum (considered as a simple harmonic oscillator) which might be mysterious or counter-intuitive is that of the *instantaneous* velocity or *instantaneous* acceleration of m. But the instantaneous velocity of the pendulum at any instant is simply the tangent line which *would be reached* as the intervals of time in the neighborhood of t are allowed to approach zero. In 1903 Peirce noted that "certain physical problems are at a standstill for want of appropriate modes of mathematical expression, and that there is need for the invention or discovery of new forms of functional relationship. Inceased attention is accordingly being directed to the wide field of the theory of functions of a complex variable."[12] New functions were needed, but this is not to say that physics was moving away from the natural classes of signs. Peirce was quite familiar with the theory of functions and its applications; for example, he used Jacobian elliptical functions to transform stereographic projections into his quincuncial map projection.[13] But he believed that intuitively clear operational definitions could be given of i (or j), and in this respect agreed with the spirit of a remark his father once made, "The imaginary square root of Algebra . . . has become the simple reality of Quaternions."[14]

Section 2: The monotonic constraint. A conservative system is one in which the total mechanical energy of the system (the kinetic energy and potential energy) neither increases nor decreases. But the laws of nature are not conservative laws. They are non-conservative laws: physical systems are usually gaining or losing energy, and equilibrium states are more the exception than the rule. Also, in general, energy is lost. Peirce put his view this way:

> Almost all the phenomena of bodies here on earth which attract our familiar notice are non-conservative, that is, are inexplicable by means of the Law of the Conservation of Energy. For they are actions which cannot be reversed. In the language of physics they are irreversible. Such, for instance, is birth, growth, life. Such is all motion resisted by friction or by the viscosity of fluids, as all terrestrial motion is. Such is the conduction of heat, combustion, capillarity, diffusion of fluids. Such is the thunderbolt, the production of high colors by a prism, the flow of rivers, the formations of bars at their mouths, the wearing of their channels; in short, substantially everything that ordinary experience reveals, except the motions of the stars. And even those we do not see to be reversed, though we may well believe them reversible.[15]

> Those non-conservative actions which seem to violate the law of energy, and which physics explains away as due to chance-action among trillions of molecules, are one and all marked by two characters. The first is that they act in one determinate direction and tend asymptotically toward bringing about an ultimate state of things. If teleological is too strong a word to apply to them, we might invent the word *finious*, to express their tendency toward a final state. The other character of non-conservative actions is that they are *irreversible*. If a falling stone, which moves under the conservative force of gravity, were suddenly to strike a perfectly elastic horizontal fixed surface, its motion would be reversed and it would move upwards to the point from which it fell with precisely the velocities it had in falling, only in reverse order. So it would be if every planet in the solar system suddenly had its motions reversed. Whatever motion conservative forces can effect, the very reverse of that motion they are equally capable of effecting.[16]

The results of Carnot, Clapeyron, Clausius, Maxwell, Rankine and others in thermodynamics show that conservative, central force laws of attraction or repulsion are insufficient to account for a number of observed effects, for example, that the temperature of a gas changes when a gas is allowed to expand freely.[17] Further, it is known that heat flow is always from hot to cold, never the other way. It is obvious in the case of living things that they are born *first,* then they live and in the *end,* die. Over the generations new forms of life evolve. The general course of events in the physical world is directional, like sign-action.[18]

When giving examples of non-conservative properties of the universe, Peirce almost invariably mentioned *viscosity.* One particular instance of viscosity with which he was very familiar was the damping of pendulums as they oscillate through the air. When two contiguous layers of air, moving at different speeds, pass each other, molecules from each layer emigrate into the other layer and tend to take on the average speed of the molecules in that region. The result is a more probable distribution of molecules than obtains were the layers to pass each other without emigration. The result of this tendency toward the more probable state is the viscosity or drag of the air. In this case, the determination is directional and seems to depend on chance rather than on habit. An analogous tendency toward the more probable state is, in the case of solids, called *Nachwirkung.*[19] Peirce thought of this non-reversible property of viscosity as being a kind of clustering phenomenon. He classified clustering phenomena into two types. *Type I clustering* is a *sifting* out of elements into separate kinds. Ten coins arranged, heads or tails, like this, H H H H H T T T T T, represent the result of sifting. As examples Peirce gave the refraction of white light into the different wave lengths and the sun's sifting of incoming meteors into different kinds of trajectories.[20] *Type II clustering* is an *emigration* into a region resulting in a more probable distribution, represented by ten coins arranged H T H T H T H T H T. Peirce believed that by far the more frequent of these two types of clustering is *emigration.*[21] In other words, there are many more cases in which configurational entropy is increased than cases in which it is not increased.

Section 3: Constraints on the mind-body interface. Mind and body obviously interact and must be parts of one system. Peirce referred to the two sides of the interface between mind and body as the two sides of a shield.[22] He knew there were millions of different kinds of substances making up the organic side and that this entire complexus was little understood.[23]

> In my second article I should consider the psychical, the pneumatic world; and here I should at first seem to be very materialistic. Naturally; for as has often been remarked, spiritualism is a sort of materialism. It seems to me that psychology since Lotze has not been pursued with very

much ability. The old associationalism of Hartley (and Gay) and Berkeley and Hume seems to have been begun with very great ability. But as for the present state of the science, look at the way in which many of the psychologists talk of consciousness. Why do they not try to find out something of the constitution of the soul, just as physicists had to begin by getting some notions of the constitution of matter? Is it because we know nothing of the *soul* except by its phenomena? The very same thing is true of matter but it does not deter physicists from investigating the constitution of matter with brilliant success. It looks to me as if, in their secret hearts, the psychologists thought that the only substance beneath manifestations of mind was certain special varieties of albuminoids or beta-amino-acids, but hadn't the courage to confess to themselves what they thought. It is a rule of the logic of hypothesis that whatever one finds an impulse to believe one should develop into so definite a form that experiment and observation may have a fair opportunity to refute it, if it be not true. The proposition so developed should thereupon be adopted provisionally and students should at once go hard to work to develop its consequences and compare them with the facts. To me it is difficult to believe that either the alpha or the beta amino acids produce Feeling, by mere physical action without any different sort of [cause]. But I would much sooner admit *that* provisionally than to rest upon consciousness, as many do, who even go so far as to *define* psychology as the science of consciousness. For it seems to me that their "consciousness," as they talk of it, is a close parallel to the substantial forms of the medieval schoolmen.[24]

Peirce also knew that there was a great deal we did not understand about the mental side of the interface if for no other reason than that many of the mental operations we perform we perform unconsciously. That we do process sense information unconsciously was, in fact, one of the main implications of the experiments Peirce and Jastrow carried out on minimal differences of sensation.[25] These experiments showed that we detect differences in the amount of pressure applied to our hand without consciously perceiving these differences. It had to be admitted, then, that the mystery of what happened at the interface extended throughout quite an interval on both sides of the interface.

Peirce did not obtain any results concerning the constraints on the mind-body interface except the following: he argued that if it were possible to have a function which was continuous but contained endless sequences followed by beginningless sequences, something analogous to this might obtain at the mind-body interface and there was no compelling reason to imagine a definite break between mind and body. Today we make computer models of the mind. What Peirce did was to make a hydrodynamic model of the interface between mind and body. He described the interface as follows:

> Consequently we must expect an endless series of transformations of energy to be followed and connected with a beginningless series of transformations in a finite time. An endless series of mechanical determinations to be followed by a beginningless series of logical determinations and *vice versa*.[26]

As a function which represents the global course of events in the mind-body system, Peirce selected the following:

$$\frac{r^2 - 4r + 3}{r - 2} = C^\theta$$

The corresponding spiral graph is shown.

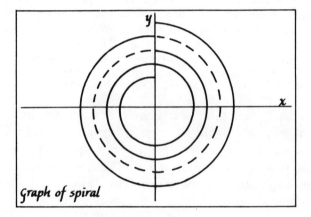

Graph of spiral

And of this spiral Peirce wrote

> The curve will start at $r = 1$ and coil outwards toward $r = 2$ making an endless series of revolutions before it reaches $r = 2$. Then it will keep right on and perform an endless series of revolutions before r becomes $2 + e$, no matter how small a distance e may be. Finally, when r becomes 3 the curve will come to an abrupt stop. This shows that although it be true that Being immediately acts only on Being and Representation immediately acts only on Representation, still there may be two endless series, whereby Being and Representation act on one another without any *tertium quid*.[27]

In the neighborhood of $r = 2$ is an unseen universe. As the radius vector decreases in magnitude the radial velocity increases (that is as we move from the region outside of 2 into the region inside of 2), representing the greater velocity of the thought series—the mental atoms being within a more subtle fluid than the physical atoms or series of events.

Section 4: Constraints in the neighborhood of the atom. At the beginning of the nineteenth century Dalton's work on gases led him in a roundabout way to calculate the relative atomic weights of a couple of dozen kinds of atoms. During the nineteenth century the most prevalent view was that while there were indeed atoms, these atoms were not necessarily hard and impenetrable and not necessarily to be conceived of as moving about in a void. One fairly representative view was that of Kekule. In 1878 Kekule expressed his view of physical reality as follows:

> As the conception of the chemical element so will also the conception of the chemical atom, as *that quantity of elementary matter which is not further divisible by chemical processes,* remain for ever. For chemistry, the question whether the chemical atoms are originally units (*einheitliche*) and absolutely indivisible beings, is of no importance. Let the proof be given that the chemical atoms are formed of particles of a finer order, or let the theory of revolving rings founded by Thomson, or some other similar conception which understands atoms to result from continuous matter, be proved in the progress of knowledge, the conception of chemical atoms will not be altered or annihilated. The chemist will always welcome an explanation of his units, because chemistry requires atoms only as a starting point, not as an end.
>
> The hypothesis of chemical quantivalence further leads to the supposition that also a considerably large number of single molecules may, through polyvalent atoms, combine to *net-like,* and if we like to say so, *sponge-like masses,* in order thus to produce those *molecular masses* which resist diffusion, and which, according to Graham's proposition, are called *colloidal* ones. The same hypothesis in the most natural manner leads to the view, already pronounced by our genial colleague, Pflüger, that such an accumulation of molecules may go further yet, and may thus form the *elements of the form* of living organisms. Of these *mass-molecules* we may perhaps suppose further that they, through the constant change of position of polyvalent atoms, show a constant change in the connected single molecules, so that the whole—and of course under generation of electricity—is in a sort of living state, particularly since, through the same change of position, adjacent molecules are drawn into the circle of combination and newly-formed ones are expelled. To follow such speculations

any further at present would, however, be equivalent to leaving the bases of facts rather too far behind us. It is generally acknowledged that the results of exact observation have the value of facts, therefore possess that degree of certainty which human knowledge can attain at all. It is further not contested that to all those laws which, independent of hypotheses on the nature of matter, are deduced from facts, nearly the same certainty must be ascribed as to facts themselves. It is just as incontestable, however, that the human mind in the positive understanding of facts does not find complete satisfaction, and that therefore natural sciences have to follow a yet further and higher aim, *that of the knowledge of the essence of matter and of the original connection of all phenomena. But the essence of matter is not accessible to any direct investigation.* We can only draw conclusions regarding it from the phenomena which are accessible to our observation. . . . Of course, the *complete* truth will never be reached in this way, or there will, at least, never exist complete certainty that our conceptions are really identical with truth. But that conception which is simplest in itself, and which in the simplest manner accounts for the greatest number of phenomena, and finally for all, will have to be considered not only as the best and most probable one, but we shall have to designate it as relatively, and we may say, humanly, true.[28]

Peirce was inclined to favor Thomson's view that atoms were vortices in a perfect fluid. A perfect fluid is by definition continuous, meaning it has no breaks in it; homogeneous, meaning it is a single kind of fluid; and perfectly elastic, meaning the fluid instantaneously occupies any potential track which otherwise would have been left in it as an open void by any displaced atom. When Thomson lectured on his view of physical reality at Johns Hopkins, Peirce tells us, he (Thomson) spoke of "a continuous perfect fluid . . . in which there are rings like smoke rings."[29] And Peirce wrote, "We make smoke rings. We make one pass through another, and perform various experiments, which give us an imperfect idea, yet some idea, of what a vortex really is."[30] During the late nineteenth century vortex-atoms were "indirectly observed" in the following way: a box is constructed about two feet by two feet by two feet; one of the six sides is fitted with an elastic membrane and a hole is made in the opposite side; the vapor from a solution of ammonium chloride is fed into one of the free sides of the box and the vapor from a solution of hydrochloric acid into another; a cloud of ammonium chloride or *sal ammoniac* forms in the box; this is then puffed out of the hole by pounding on the elastic membrane; the smoke rings formed are what vortex atoms look like; by sending smoke rings from a second box, two rings can be seen to pass through one another, rebound off one another and change size; by not putting one of the ingredients in one of the boxes one of the two rings would not be seen though its effect would be seen, in which case one saw what was called the "unseen universe." When this nineteenth-century version of the Wilson cloud chamber sends out a continuous series of interpenetrating smoke rings we have a picture of Peirce's model of the atom (this atom may be envisaged as a vortex within the mind-body hydrodynamic fluid). Peirce described this part of the continuum as follows:

> Now I take up the somewhat indefinite modification of the vortical hypothesis of atoms by which I mean that without definitely adopting that hypothesis I suppose that atoms are of a nature more or less analogous to that. The electron theory is for example more or less analogous to the vortical theory of atoms, for both suppose atoms to have a multitude of parts. Let us suppose then that a visible motion is more or less converted into motions of electrons or into the motions of that underlying fluid whose vortices are atoms. And just as we suppose ordinary fluids to consist of molecules and ultimately of atoms, let us suppose that that underlying fluid has a similar constitution so that a motion in it becomes transformed in part into motions of its atoms or quasi-electrons. But these in their turn consist of vortices or some other forms of a still underlying fluid with a similar constitution. Let there be an endless series then of transformations of motions of subtler and subtler fluids.[31]

In phanerochemistry we described a sense in which there was only one basic kind of element, that element having a valency of three. Peirce suggested the same might be true of ordinary chemical elements. This might be, he thought, some acyclic three-dimensional configuration capable of forming compounds (or "chemical atoms") with higher valencies by threeing. As for "chemical atoms" such as argon, with a valency of zero, Peirce wrote, "Thus, we may imagine the atoms of argon to be really formed of four triads, thus."[32]

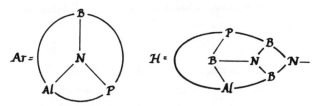

Atoms with valencies of zero and one

(Similar to a tetrahedron? See diagram.) An atom with a valency of one is also shown. And an element with a valency of *two,* he said, can be represented simply by imagining any single bond of the argon type of configuration broken.[33]

In his paper entitled "On the Chemical Theory of Interpenetration,"[34] Peirce put forward the hypothesis that matter was continuous and that atoms could interpenetrate one another. (Kant had put forward the theory that matter was continuous and that portions of matter could interpenetrate other portions.) The term "interpenetrate" could mislead the reader, because it suggests that one atom goes into another. But what Peirce had in mind was that the mathematical functions which represent forces in the atomic realm were continuous functions, and no integers (as those representing atomic weights) emerged from continuous functions except in the case of something like wave motion where interference patterns gave rise to orders of spectra.[35] To this must be added the fact that values obtained for the atomic weights were not exact values. Stas's determinations of the relative atomic weights showed these to be not exact multiples of the weight of hydrogen, but *approximate* multiples of the weight of hydrogen. And Lord Rayleigh's investigations of the specific gravity of nitrogen indicated that the atomic weight of this element is *approximately* 14.096/16.000 that of oxygen.[36] So Peirce looked upon any hypothesis to the effect that the atom was continuous as fitting *the map* and as, therefore, a reasonable hypothesis.

The great *alternative* hypothesis was that matter was discontinuous, impenetrable, and rigidly deterministic in nature, and this alternative hypothesis Peirce viewed as an unreasonable hypothesis.

> We have no logical right to suppose that absolute impenetrability, or the exclusive occupancy of space, belongs to molecules or to atoms. It is an unwarranted hypothesis. . . .[37] No analogy of known phenomena exists to excuse such a wanton violation of the principle of continuity . . .[38] [Putting forward the hypothesis that matter is composed of solid, homogeneous bits of matter having] a closed surface unalterable in shape and size.[39]

The best argument against the hypothesis that matter is continuous came from the kinetic theory of gases. The kinetic theory postulated that gases are composed of millions of rapidly moving molecules which rebound off each other and off the walls of their container. Each molecule bounces off other molecules or off the wall at the instant of impact *of the surfaces* involved, it being supposed that a gas molecule has a particular size and shape (even if it were a compound molecule, this would be so under this supposition, for in this case the molecule is conceived to be a little *plenum*). This billiard-ball model was very successful in accounting for the perfect gas laws, most especially for the relationship $(3/2) PV = kT$. In 1873 Van der Waals introduced a term into gas law equations which represented (in theory) the exact size of the gas molecule in the system, one term representing the size of the oxygen molecule, another representing the size of the nitrogen molecule, etc. These terms were very helpful in accounting for certain observed departures from the perfect gas laws, departures dependent upon the kind of gas under investigation. In the field of kinetic theory (which Peirce called the *dynamics of clustering*)[40] the most famous theorist of the nineteenth century was Clausius. And in this field, Peirce said, it is Clausius's *theorem of the virial* which ought to be the *cynosure* (that upon which we ought to focus our attention as a guiding [pole] star).[41] The *virial* is an expression representing the total kinetic energy of a system of particles. In his 1870 paper, "A Mechanical Theorem Applicable to Heat," Clausius wrote the virial as

$$\tfrac{1}{2} \sum (X_x + Y_y + Z_z)$$

and the theorem of the virial as

$$\text{HEAT} = -\tfrac{1}{2} \sum (X_x + Y_y + Z_z) + \tfrac{3}{2}PV.$$

What this theorem enables us to do, Peirce pointed out, is to account for all the global properties of gases such as quantity of heat lost or gained, temperature, pressure, volume, density, etc., in terms of the positions of the particles, their masses, and the force laws which operate between them. These force laws would be probabilistic and complex, but whatever advantages might be gained by supposing an atom to have a definite size and surface can just as well be gained by supposing that the distribution of forces in the system are such as to reach maximal values at a specified radius.[42]

Section 5: Further constraints on the atom. In section 1, we mentioned that *things,* too, were signs and obeyed the same *would-be* constraints as laws. An atom is a thing, but like any other thing, it is properly thought of (and can only be thought of) as a sign. This means that like a table or a chair or any other object, the atom cannot be thought of except along such lines as: if so and so conditions were to obtain, then such and such *would be* observed.

When the atom is approached from the point of view of classical logic, the atom is envisaged as either having or not having any named property, and as never both having and not having a given property; that is, the law of excluded middle and the law of non-contradiction are taken to apply to the atom. The atom, as so envisaged, is an existing substance which has properties, or is comprised of properties, and these properties are themselves envisaged as existents just like the substance of which they are properties.

When the atom is approached from the point of view of Peirce's system of logic, or semiotic, it is envisaged quite differently. The properties of the atom are seen as sets of real possibilities or potentialities which become partially actualized upon the occasion that we observe the atom. In general, actuality cannot exhaust possibilities,[43] so we anticipate that any actually observed state of the atom would be a selection from possible states; this applies also in the case of a single property; a single property, Peirce said, being more than what it is at any instant.[44] It is anticipated, also, that at times the atom will assume new, unexpected states, display signs of growth and development, and, amidst all this, continue to assume favored states like the clustering of ideas, and this with a regularity midway between that exhibited by the elements of chemistry and the elements of phanerochemistry. The properties of the atom, as pure possibilities, have no individual identity: *identity*, Peirce said, belongs properly only to seconds.[45]

The properties of the atom are not expected to obey the law of excluded middle or the law of non-contradiction.[46] The properties of the atom are expected to obey the law of continuity. Peirce frequently pointed out that no part of a continuum has to be or is wholly A or wholly not-A.[47] Neither the law of excluded middle nor the law of non-contradiction applies to *anything* general and the atom is general except at that moment of observation at which point it becomes fully determinate.[48] The atom is, then, except at the moment of observation, a general or collection of real possibilities. Upon the occasion that the atom is observed, that is, upon the occasion that an actually existing state of the atom is observed, then there is a discontinuity and the laws of excluded middle and non-contradiction apply to the atom.[49] Once, in an Hegelian frame of mind, Peirce said that the logic of freedom or possibility is that it shall annul itself.[50] Another way Peirce put it was to say that *time* permits existents, which as seconds obey the laws of classical logic, to evade these laws.[51]

The purpose of the preceding five sections has been to put forward the transuasional argument that such constraints as apply to thought may apply to nature. Given this conjecture, what might be done next is to (1) work more on Peirce's system of logic so as to improve our understanding of it; (2) review some of the basic concepts of mathematics and the idioscopic sciences; (3) identify exactly from which families of indeterminate relations these basic concepts spring; and (4) come up with some original hypotheses concerning these sciences, hypotheses which emerge from using Peirce's system and which are likely not to have been discovered without having used his system. This fourth project is feasible because there is no source for original ideas except more general ideas coupled with a knowledge of local constraints.

The conjecture that important isomorphisms might obtain between thought and the world of quantum mechanics may strike the reader as an astonishing conjecture. In 1896 Peirce wrote, "it would certainly be astonishing if it should turn out that the material constituents of phenomena were coextensive with formal ideas."[52]

If a philosophical name were to be attached to Peirce's theory of discovery or his system of logic or his semiotic, the best would be *Pragmaticism*.

NOTES

The major sources referred to in the following notes are:

Kenneth Laine Ketner et al., eds., *A Comprehensive Bibliography and Index of the Published Works of Charles Sanders Peirce with a Bibliography of Secondary Studies* (Greenwich, Conn.: Johnson Associates, Inc., 1977). Items written by Peirce are designated by numbers such as P 00040. Items written about Peirce by his contemporaries are designated by numbers such as 0 00058. Other secondary material is designated by numbers such as S 00054.

Charles Hartshorne and Paul Weiss, eds., *Collected Papers of Charles Sanders Peirce*, vols. I-VI (1931-35; rpt. Cambridge, Mass.: The Belknap Press of Harvard University, 1965), [S 00643]; and Arthur W. Burks, ed., vols. VII-VIII (1958; rpt. Cambridge, Mass.: The Belknap Press of Harvard University, 1966), [S 00216]. References to this work are designated by volume and section number; 7.97 means volume VII, paragraph 97.

Max H. Fisch et al., eds., *Writings of Charles S. Peirce: A Chronological Edition*, vols. I and II (Bloomington, Indiana: The Indiana University Press, 1982). References to this are designated *W*, Roman numeral (volume number), page number.

Carolyn Eisele, ed., *The New Elements of Mathematics by Charles S. Peirce*, vols. I-IV (The Hague: Mouton, 1976), [S 00411]. References to this are designated *NEM*, followed by volume and page number.

William D. Whitney et al., eds., *The Century Dictionary and Cyclopedia* (New York: The Century Co., 1889), [P 00373]. References to this are designated *CD* followed by page number.

Richard S. Robin, ed., *Annotated Catalogue of the Papers of Charles S. Peirce* (Amherst: The University of Massachusetts Press, 1967), [S 01205]; "The Peirce Papers: A Supplementary Catalogue," *Transactions of the Charles S. Peirce Society*, VII, No. 1 (Winter 1971), 37-57, [S 01106]. References to the Peirce manuscripts are designated by a number such as MS 278-4 which means manuscript number 278, page 4. References to the Peirce correspondence are designated by L numbers such as L 24.

Kenneth Laine Ketner and James Edward Cook, eds., *Charles Sanders Peirce: Contributions to the Nation*, Part One: 1869-1893, Part Two: 1894-1900, Part Three: 1901-1908 (Lubbock: Texas Tech Press, 1975, 1978, 1979), [S 00753]. References to this work are designated as *N* followed by volume and page number.

Transactions of the Charles S. Peirce Society: A Quarterly Journal in American Philosophy. References to this are designated *Transactions* followed by volume and page number.

Preface

1. Morris Cohen, ed., *Chance, Love and Logic* (New York: Barnes and Noble, Inc., 1923), p. viii [S 00279].

2. Philip P. Wiener and Frederic H. Young, *Studies in the Philosophy of Charles Sanders Peirce* (Cambridge, Mass.: Harvard University Press, 1952), p. v [S 01549].

3. James K. Feibleman, *An Introduction to Peirce's Philosophy Interpreted as a System* (London: George Allen and Unwin Ltd., 1960) [S 00451].

4. Murray G. Murphey, *The Development of Peirce's Philosophy* (Cambridge; Harvard University Press, 1961) [S 01001].

5. Karl-Otto Apel, *Charles S. Peirce from Pragmatism to Pragmaticism*, trans. John Michael Krois (Amherst: University of Massachusetts Press, 1981).

6. Raymond M. Herbenick, "Peirce on Systems Theory," *Transactions* 6, No. 2 (Spring 1970), 97.

7. Joseph Esposito, *Evolutionary Metaphysics: The Development of Peirce's Theory of Categories* (Athens, Ohio: Ohio University Press, 1980), preface and introduction.

8. Paul Weiss, "The Essence of Peirce's System," *Journal of Philosophy* 37 (1940), 353–364 [S 01494].

9. Feibleman, p. 291.

10. Justus Buchler, "The Accidents of Peirce's System," *Journal of Philosophy* 37 (1940), 364–369 [S 00191].

11. Feibleman, foreword.

12. Irwin C. Lieb, "New Studies in the Philosophy of Charles S. Peirce," *Review of Metaphysics* 8 (1954), 293 [S 00840].

13. José F. Mora, "Peirce's Conception of Architectonic and Related Views," *Philosophy and Phenomenological (Research) Thought* (1955), pp. 351–359.

Introduction

1. 4.2 (1898).

2. *W*, I, 104 (1863).

3. *W*, 306 (1865).

4. *W*, I, 223 (1865); and see *W*, I, 404 (1866).

5. a) 1870: "Description of a Notation for the Logic of Relatives, Resulting from an Amplification of the Conceptions of Boole's Calculus of Logic," *W*, II, 359; 3.45 [P 00052].

b) 1875: "On the Application of Logical Analysis to Multiple Algebra," 3.150 [P 00090].

c) 1880: "On the Algebra of Logic," 3.154 [P 00167].

d) 1881: "Linear Associative Algebra," 3.289 [P 00188].

e) 1883: "The Logic of Relatives," Note B in *Johns Hopkins Studies in Logic*, ed. C. S. Peirce (Boston: Little, Brown & Co., 1883), pp. 187–203; 3.328 [P 00242].

f) 1885: "On the Algebra of Logic: A Contribution to the Philosophy of Notation," 3.359 [P 00296].

6. 4.5 (1898).

7. Hilary Putnam, "Peirce the Logician," *Historia Mathematica* 9:3 (1982), 290–301.

8. See, for example, C. S. Peirce's 1873 paper "On the Theory of Errors of Observation" [P 00077], where he expresses the conditional probability that B will happen given that A happens $\rho(B \cap A)/\rho(A)$ in terms of the logic of relations $[A_c B]/[A]$.

9. See "On the Application of Logical Analysis to Multiple Algebra," 3.150 (1875) [P 00090]; 3.323 (1882); and *NEM*, III, 1136 (1909).

10. E. Schröder, *Vorlesungen über die Algebra der Logik (Exakte Logik)* (Leipzig: B. G. Teubner, 1890, 1891, 1895). See especially Volume III, *Algebra und Logik der Relative*.

11. For example, consider the symbols $\prod$ and $\sum$. In his 1870 paper Peirce used the symbol $\prod$ for a logical product $(A \cap B)$ and the symbol $\sum$ for a logical sum $(A \cup B)$. After quantifiers were invented (by Frege in section 8 of the *Begriffschrift* [1879] and O. H. Mitchell in "On a New Algebra of Logic" in *Studies in Logic*, p. 73), Peirce used $\prod_i x_i$ to mean what we write today as (x)Fx or $\forall$xFx and $\sum_i x_i$ to mean ($\exists$ x)Fx or $\exists$xFx. Peirce's pi-sigma notation was standard at the turn of the century and continued in use for some time. For example, the pi-sigma notation was used in Herman Weyl's *Philosophy of Mathematics and Natural Science* (Princeton: Princeton University Press, 1949). Originally published in *Handbuch der Philosophie: Philosophie der Mathematik und Naturwissenschaft* (R. Oldenbourg, 1927), pp. 6–18.

12. 4.373 (1902).

13. 1.368 (1890).

14. 1.42 (1892), 5.38 (1903).

15. 2.141 (1902).

16. 5.38 (1903).

17. 1.544 (1903), 1.42 (1892), 1.540 (1903).

18. *W*, I, 352 (1866); 2.112 (1882), 6.218 (1898), 6.365 (1898); Charles S. Peirce, review of *Basal Concepts in Philosophy*, by Alexander T. Ormond, *The Nation* 59 (July 1894), 34–35, rpt. in *N*, II, 63 [P 00574]. Charles S. Peirce, rev. of *The Origin and Significance of Hegel's Logic: A General Introduction to Hegel's System*, by J. B. Baillie, *The Nation* 75 (Nov. 1902), 390, rpt. in *N*, III, 103 [P 00991].

19. Josiah Royce, *Basic Writings of Josiah Royce*, ed. John J. Mcdermott (Chicago: University of Chicago Press, 1969), I, 381; II, 657, 673.

20. Royce, II, 678; *NEM*, III, 431 (1900).

21. 8.117 (1900).

22. Royce, II, 689.

23. Royce, II, 1161.

24. Karl-Otto Apel, *Charles S. Peirce from Pragmatism to Pragmaticism*, trans. John Michael Krois (Amherst: University of Massachusetts Press, 1981) pp. 9–10, 191–196.

25. William Whewell, *The History of the Inductive Sciences* (London: Cass, 1967), 3 vols; *The Philosophy of the Inductive Sciences* (London: Cass, 1967), 2 vols.

26. 6.604 (1893). (Peirce's italics.)

27. *W*, II, 340 (1869).

28. Rudolf Carnap, *Logical Foundations of Probability* (Chicago: University of Chicago Press, 1950), *The Continuum of Inductive Methods* (Chicago: The University of Chicago Press, 1952); Hans Reichenbach, *The Theory of Probability*, trans. E. H. Hutten and M. Reichenbach (Berkeley, Calif.: The University of California Press, 1949, 1971); William Kneale, *Probability and Induction* (Oxford: Clarendon Press, 1949); G. H. von Wright, *The Logical Problem of Induction* (Oxford: B. Blackwell, 1957).

29. H. Butterfield, *The Origins of Modern Science* (London: Bell, 1949).

30. Thomas Kuhn, *The Structure of Scientific Revolutions* (Chicago: University of Chicago Press, 1962).

31. Owen Gingerich, ed., *The Nature of Scientific Discovery* (Washington: Smithsonian Institution Press, 1975).

32. Gerald Holton, "Mainsprings of Scientific Discovery," *The Nature of Scientific Discovery,* ed. Owen Gingerich (Washington: Smithsonian Institution Press, 1975), p. 201.

33. Ibid., p. 203.

34. Thomas Nickles, ed., *Scientific Discovery, Logic and Rationality,* LVI and *Scientific Discovery: Case Studies,* LX, *Boston Studies in the Philosophy of Science* (Dordrecht, Holland: D. Reidel, 1980).

35. Ibid., LVI, 2.

36. Ibid., LVI, 1.

37. 4.7 (1906).

38. *Transactions* XI, No. 3 (Summer 1975).

39. Max H. Fisch, "Introduction: Peirce and the History of Science Society," *Transactions* XI, No. 3 (Summer 1975), 146 [S 00487].

40. Pierre S. Laplace, *Celestial Mechanics,* trans. Nathaniel Bowditch (Bronx, N.Y.: Chelsea Publishing Co., Inc., 1966).

41. Nathaniel Bowditch, introd. to *Celestial Mechanics,* by Pierre Laplace. (Bronx, N.Y.: Chelsea Publishing Co., Inc., 1966).

42. Benjamin Peirce, *Analytic Mechanics* (Boston: Little, Brown and Co., 1885).

43. Ibid., p. vi.

44. Benjamin Peirce, *Ideality in the Physical Sciences* (Boston: Little, Brown and Co., 1881), p. 11.

45. Ibid., p. 76. This equation states that the total momentum in a closed system is zero. (It is a way of expressing the law of the conservation of mechanical energy.)

46. Ibid. V. F. Lenzen, *Benjamin Peirce and the U. S. Coast Survey* (San Francisco: San Francisco Press, Inc., 1968), p. 20.

47. Victor F. Lenzen, "Charles S. Peirce as Mathematical Physicist," unpublished draft, in Fisch's file "Lenzen," p. 9.

48. Charles S. Peirce, review of *Modern Chromatics: With Applications to Art and Industry,* by Ogden N. Rood, *The Nation* 29 (October 1879), 260, rpt. in *N,* I, 58–61 [P 00149].

49. H. A. Rowland, "Concave Gratings for Optical Purposes," *The American Journal of Science* XXVI (July-December 1883), 93.

50. Charles S. Peirce, *Photometric Researches, Made in the Years 1872–1875; Annals of the Astronomical Observatory of Harvard College* (Leipzig: Wilhelm Englemann), vol. 9 (1878).

51. For a further description of this instrument and for frontispiece, see: Johann C. F. Zöllner, *Photometrische Untersuchungen* (Leipzig; Wilhelm Englemann, 1865).

52. Charles S. Peirce, review of *Modern Chromatics: With Applications to Art and Industry.* And see Charles S. Peirce, review of *William Herschel and His Work,* by James Sime, *The Nation* 72 (January 1901), 72–73, rpt. in *N,* III, 20 [P 00782].

53. 7.59 (1882).

54. 7.62 (1882).

55. 7.63 (1882).

56. *NEM,* III, xxxii (1885); and see ms 671 (1911), pp. 1–3.

57. 2.109 (1902).

58. *NEM,* IV, 185 (1904).

59. *NEM,* III, 867 (1909).
60. 4.116 (1894), 8.343 (1908).
61. 1.444 (1896); MS 900–22 (1896).
62. MS 449–26 (1903).
63. MS 793–20 (1905).
64. 5.488 (1907).
65. 1.559 (1867).
66. 2.93 (1902).
67. 1.191 (1903).
68. 1.559 (1867); *NEM,* IV, 376 (undated); MSS 4–24 (1904), 774–3 (1904), 595–23 (1895), 774–9 (1904).
69. MS 449–26 (1903).
70. Max H. Fisch, "Peirce's Arisbe: The Greek Influence in His Later Philosophy," *Transactions* VII, No. 4 (Fall 1971), 187 [S 00482]. Peirce's life is here divided into three periods: (1) the Cambridge period (1851–1870), (2) the Cosmopolitan period (1870–1887), and (3) the Arisbe period (1887–1914).
71. MSS 425 to 434 (1902); 2.93 (1902). These terms are mentioned by E. Freeman in his *The Categories of Charles Peirce,* 1934 [S 00521], p. 23, section 26; and in J. Esposito's *Evolutionary Metaphysics* (Athens, Ohio: Ohio University Press, 1941), p. 196.
72. 8.302 (1902), 8.377 (1908); L 463:147.
73. Charles S. Peirce, review of *Studies in Deductive Logic,* by W. Stanley Jevons, *The Nation* 32 (March 1881), 227, rpt. in *N,* I, 64 [P 00198]. And see *W,* I, 486; 6.7 (1891), 1.1 (1890), 1.539 (1903), 2.1 (1902), 7.60 (1902), 7.161 (1902), 8.275 (1902); MSS 793–16 (1905), 1334–50 (1905).
74. 2.107 (1902).
75. 4.373 (1902).
76. Charles S. Peirce, review of *Molecules and the Molecular Theory of Matter,* by A. D. Risteen, *The Nation* 62 (February 1896), 147, rpt. in *N,* II, 129 [P 00625].
77. *NEM,* IV, 37 (1902); 1.286 (1904), 2.227 (c. 1897); and see 8.303 (1909).

1. Speculative Grammar (1)

1. Norwood Hanson, *Patterns of Discovery* (Cambridge: Cambridge University Press, 1958), p. 86.
2. 5.189 (1903).
3. Thomas Nickles, ed., *Boston Studies,* LVI, 23, 225; LX, 190.
4. 5.189 (1903).
5. Nicholas Rescher, *Peirce's Philosophy of Science: Critical Studies in His Theory of Induction and Scientific Method* (Notre Dame, Indiana: University of Notre Dame Press, 1978).
6. Martin Curd, "The Logic of Discovery: An Analysis of Three Approaches," *Boston Studies,* LVI, 213.
7. *NEM,* III, 203 (1911).
8. Martin Curd, p. 213.
9. *W,* I, 180 (1865).
10. *W,* I, 180 (1865).
11. 7.218 (1901).
12. Charles S. Peirce, *Photometric Researches* (Leipzig: *Annals of the Harvard College Observatory,* vol. 9, 1878), p. 178 [P 00118].

13. *NEM,* IV, 319 (1906); and see 2.694 (1883).

14. 5.590 (1903).

15. 2.96 (1902).

16. 2.776 (1902).

17. 5.591 (1898); and see 5.603 (1898).

18. *NEM,* IV, 320 (1906); and see 2.776 (1902), 7.218 (1901); and Paul Anderson and Max Fisch, eds., *Philosophy in America* (New York: Appleton-Century-Crofts, Inc., 1939), p. 443 [S 00030].

19. *NEM,* III, 204 (1911).

20. John William Huggett, "Charles Peirce's Search for a Method," Diss., University of Toronto, 1954, Abstract; and see S 00698, p. 211.

21. Martin Curd, p. 214.

22. *NEM,* IV, 320 (1906).

23. *NEM,* III, 205 (1911).

24. *NEM,* IV, 320 (1906).

25. 5.581 (1898).

26. *NEM,* IV, 320 (1906).

27. *CD,* 1104.

28. 5.581 (1898); *W,* II, 342 (1869).

29. Peter S. Stevens, *Patterns in Nature* (New York: Penguin Books, 1977).

30. Johannes Kepler, *The Secret of the Universe,* trans. A. M. Duncan (New York: Abaris Books, 1981).

31. *NEM,* III, 206 (1911).

32. 2.421 (1893); and see 2.364 (1902).

33. 2.419 (1893); and see 1.447 (1896), 2.430 (1893), 4.582 (1906), 4.664 (1909).

34. 5.583 (1898).

35. Arthur Berry, *A Short History of Astronomy* (New York: Dover, 1961), p. 196. Berry says the quotation is from Kepler's *Epitome,* Book IV, part 2.

36. Sir William Thomson and Peter Guthrie Tait, *Elements of Natural Philosophy* (Cambridge: Cambridge University Press, 1912), p. 136.

37. D. A. S. Fraser, *Statistics: An Introduction* (New York: John Wiley and Sons, Inc., 1958), p. 119.

Let $x_1, \ldots, x_n$ be a sample from a probability distribution for which $E\{m(x)\}$ exists. Let $E\{m(x)\} = \mu_m$. *The law of large numbers says that for any small* δ,

$$\Pr\left\{\mu_m - \delta < \frac{1}{n}\sum_{i=1}^{n} M(x_i) < \mu_m + \delta\right\}$$

approaches 1 *as* $n \to \infty$. That is, the probability that the large-sample average is within a small neighborhood of its mean can be made arbitrarily close to 1 by considering a sufficiently large sample.

2. Speculative Grammar (2)

1. 2.326 (1902).

2. 1.302 (1894).

3. 1.417 (1896).

4. *NEM,* IV, 332 (1898).

5. *NEM,* IV, 334 (1898).

6. 7.540 (c. 1897).

7. *NEM*, III, 834 (1905).

8. 1.286 (1904); and see 8.303 (1909).

9. 2.227 (c. 1897).

10. 2.27 (1902), 6.104 (1892), 6.110 (1892), 6.127 (1892); MS 141–10 (1899).

11. 5.213–5.263 (1868).

12. *NEM*, IV, 310 (1895).

13. Charles S. Peirce, review of *The Science of Mechanics: A Critical and Histori-cal Exposition of Its Principles,* by Ernst Mach, *The Nation* 57 (October 1893), 251–252; rpt. in *N,* I, 187–191; 8.132 (1901); *W,* I, 473 (1866), *W,* II, 191 (1868).

14. *W,* II, 345 (1869).

15. *NEM*, III, 493 (1907).

16. *NEM*, IV, 346 (1898); 7.643 (1903).

17. 1.427 (1896), 1.474 (1896), 1.477 (1896); *NEM,* I, 243 (1912), *NEM,* IV, 309–310 (1895), *NEM,* IV, 333 (1898).

18. 1.428–1.440 (1896).

19. 1.405 (c. 1890), 6.59–6.65 (1892), 6.595 (1893), 7.189 (1901), 7.511 (1898).

20. 1.459 (1896).

21. Howard E. Gruber, "Creativity: An Evolving Systems Approach," *Boston Studies,* vol. LX, p. 124.

22. 4.552 note (1906); *NEM,* III, 770 (1900), *NEM,* IV, 48 (1902).

23. 5.92 (1903). Peirce's secondness resembles contemporary notions of *os-tensive* definitions. See, e.g., W. V. Quine and J. S. Ullian, *The Web of Belief,* 2nd ed. (New York: Random House, 1970), p. 24.

24. *NEM,* IV, 308; MS 717 (1895); *NEM,* IV, 333 (1898).

25. 5.469 (1907).

26. *NEM,* IV, 308 (1895).

27. Kenneth Laine Ketner, ed., "A Brief Intellectual Autobiography by Charles Sanders Peirce," *American Journal of Semiotics* 2, nos. 1–2 (1983), p. 72 [L 107.22].

28. 5.469 (1907).

29 1.351 (1903), 1.288 (1904), 5.469 (1907).

30. 1.303 (1894); Corresponding to medads, monads, dyads, and triads are the graphs ●—○ , •—— , —•— , and —< , respectively. For a brief account of some aspects of Peirce's graph theory, see Kenneth L. Ketner, "Peirce's Most Lucid and Interesting Paper: 'An Introduction to Cenopythagoreanism,'" *Deutsche Gesellschaft für Semiotik* (1985). Ketner believes (because the positive sciences generally depend on mathematics?) that phanerochemistry depends on mathematics, specifically on, say, topology or graph theory. This cannot be entirely true because mathematics itself is an object of cognition and must therefore meet the conditions of the understanding. In any case graph theory is important because it is a form of exact logic or the logic of relations, which exhibits in an exceptionally clear way important relations of common interest to graph theory and phanerochemistry.

31. 1.303 (1894).

32. 1.295 (1905).

33. 1.296 (1905).

34. 1.297 (1905).

35. 1.298 (1905); and see footnote.

36. *NEM*, IV, 338 (1898); 1.347 (1902), 4.309 (1902); MS 482 (1896); H. Herzberger, *Pragmatism and Purpose: Essays Presented to Thomas A. Goudge*, ed. J. G. Slater, T. Wilson, and T. W. Summer (Toronto: University of Toronto Press, 1981), pp. 41–58; and see J. Brunning, "Peirce's Development of the Algebra of Relations," diss., University of Toronto, 1981.

37. 1.563 (1867).

38. Hilary Putnam, "Peirce the Logician," *Historia Mathematica* 9, No. 3 (1982), 296.

39. 1.548 note (1867).

40. *CD*, p. 4701 (1898); and see *W*, I, 518 (1866); 4.235 (1902).

41. *NEM*, IV, 162 (1903).

42. *NEM*, IV, 162–163 (1902).

43. Charles S. Peirce gave this first example (concerning the plane cubic curves) at 1.365. He mentioned that the conics are paired with straight lines; the equation $3x^2 + 2x = 0$ exemplifies this, its graph shown here.

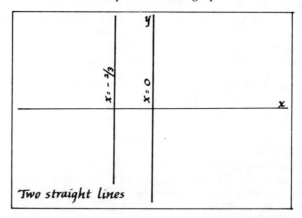

At MSS 304–34 (1903) and 478–30 (1903), C. S. P. indicates that he took the terms *genuine* and *degenerate* from the geometry of plane curves.

44. 1.353 (1880).

45. 1.288 (1904), 1.351 (1903), 5.469 (1907).

46. 1.548 (1867).

47. 1.468 (1896).

48. 1.482 (1896).

49. 5.72 (1903).

50. *NEM*, IV, 68 (1902).

51. *NEM*, III, 835 (1905).

52. Aristotle, *Metaphysics* 987.

53. 8.376 (1908).

54. Herbert W. Schneider, "Fourthness," *Studies in the Philosophy of Charles Sanders Peirce*, ed. Philip P. Weiner and Frederick H. Young (Cambridge: Harvard University Press, 1952), [S 00263].

55. 4.310 (1902); and see 1.291 (1906).

56. 1.453 (1896); *W*, I, 352. [C. S. P. uses lower case "n."]

57. *NEM,* IV, 21 (1902), 1.521 (1903).
58. 2.186 (1902).
59. 2.227 (c. 1897), 6.488 (1908); MS 280–7 (1905).
60. 5.587 (1898); and see Max Black, "Vagueness," *Philosophy of Science* 4 (1937), 431 [S 00120].

3. Speculative Grammar (3)

1. Max H. Fisch, "Just *How* General Is Peirce's General Theory of Signs?," *American Journal of Semiotics* 2, Nos. 1–2 (1983), 55. As an introduction to Semiotic, the reader might take a look at John Deely, *Introducing Semiotic: Its History and Doctrine* (Bloomington: Indiana University Press, 1982), or Douglas Greenlee, *Peirce's Concept of Sign* (The Hague: Mouton, 1973) [S 00587].
2. 3.433 (1896).
3. *NEM,* IV, 309 (1895). Peirce's brackets.
4. 2.274 (1902).
5. 2.303 (1902).
6. *NEM,* III, 233 (1909).
7. *NEM,* III, 839 (1909).
8. 1.558 (1867).
9. 2.233 (1903).
10. 4.537 (1906).
11. 8.333–8.343 (1904).
12. 2.275 (1902).
13. *NEM,* III, 886 (1908).
14. 2.235–2.237 (1903).
15. 2.242 (1903).
16. Peirce's account of these six classes of signs and the other four classes of signs follows 2.254 (1903).
17. A spectral ghost is a spectral line (or set of lines) which should not be where they are, but are there due to defects in a diffraction grating. "Gitter" is another term for "diffraction grating." In 1879 Peirce discovered that the ghosts in Rutherfurd's spectra were caused by defects in the ruling engine which cut the gitter. See P 00134.
18. 2.330 (1902).
19. *NEM,* IV, 241; MS 517 (c. 1904).
20. *NEM,* IV, 261; MS 517 (c. 1904).
21. 2.267 (1903).
22. 2.269 (1902).
23. 2.270 (1903).

4. Critical Logic (1)

1. *NEM,* III, 757 (1893).
2. MS 312 (1903).
3. 2.267 (1903), 3.559 (1898), 3.364 (1885), 5.579 (1898), 5.581 (1898); *NEM,* IV, 275 (c. 1895), *NEM,* IV, 47 (1902).
4. 4.234 (1902); *NEM,* IV, 1 (1901).
5. MS 94 (1894).
6. *NEM,* II, 345 (1903).

7. David Hume, *An Enquiry Concerning Human Understanding* (New York: Liberal Arts Press, 1955), section IV, part 1, p. 40.

8. *NEM*, IV, 58 (1902).

9. *NEM*, IV, 58 (1902).

10. 4.85 (1893). In *The Web of Belief,* Quine and Ullian say *implication* is what makes our system of beliefs cohere, p. 40.

11. Charles S. Peirce, review of *Compte, Mill and Spencer: An Outline of Philosophy,* by John Watson, *The Nation* 60 (April 1895), 284–285, rpt. in *N,* II, 102 [P 00599]; 2.96 (1902).

12. 1.137 ff. (1898), 1.150 (1892), 4.531 (1906), 5.265 (1868), 6.595 (1893).

13. 3.426 (1896), 3.560 (1898), 6.286 (1894), 7.220 (1901); MSS 430–7 ff. (1902), 691–93 (1901), 693 b–342 (1904); and see MSS 787–4 (1895), 1337–4 (1892).

14. 5.363 (1877).

15. *NEM*, II, 346 (1884).

16. Charles S. Peirce, "Some Studies in Reasoning," review of *Riemann and His Significance for the Development of Modern Mathematics,* by Felix Klein, *The Nation* 61 (July 1895), 14–16, rpt. in *N,* II, 106 [P 00601].

17. 2.268 (1903); and see 2.700 (1883).

18. 1.65 (1896), 2.267 (1903), 4.613 (1908), 7.204 (1901); MSS 691–100 var 11 (1901).

19. *NEM*, IV, 49 (1902).

20. *NEM*, IV, 318 (1906).

21. 4.233 (1902).

22. *NEM*, III, 343 (1903).

23. *NEM*, III, 622 (1908).

24. 4.353 (c. 1903); and see *NEM,* IV, 1 (1901).

25. James R. Newman, ed., *The World of Mathematics* (New York: Simon and Schuster, 1956), I, 574 (my italics).

26. See Carolyn Eisele's numerous articles on this subject, such as "C. S. Peirce's Search for a Method in Mathematics and the History of Science," *Transactions* 11, No. 3 (Summer 1975) [S 00408]; "Modern Mathematical Exactitude in Peirce's 'Doctrine of Exact Philosophy,' " *Proceedings of CSP Bicentennial International Congress* (Lubbock, Texas: Texas Tech Press, 1981), pp. 155–168 [S 00411]; "Mathematical Methodology in the thought of Charles S. Peirce," *Historia Mathematica* 9, No. 3 (1982), 333–341.

27. Kenneth Laine Ketner, "Carolyn Eisele's Place in Peirce Studies," *Historia Mathematica* 9, No. 3 (1982), 328.

28. This is the opening sentence of B. Peirce's *Linear Associative Algebra* often quoted by C. S. P. [P 00188] (1881); and see *NEM,* III, 343 (1903).

29. Charles S. Peirce, "Mathematical Functions," review of *Theory of Functions of a Complex Variable,* by A. R. Forsyth, *The Nation* 58 (March 1894), 197–199, rpt. in *N,* II, 44 [P 00566].

30. 4.239 (1897); *NEM,* III, 1133 (1909).

31. *NEM*, III, 64 (1897).

32. Ibid.

33. Ibid.

34. 1.417 (1896).

35. *NEM*, IV, 160 (1903).

36. 2.267 (1903); and see 7.207 (1901).

37. 3.162 (1881), 3.472–3.474 (1897).

38. Victor Lenzen, *Benjamin Peirce and the U. S. Coast Survey* (San Francisco: San Francisco Press, Inc., 1968), p. 20.

39. That Boole permitted this expression is clear, since for the equation $v(1 - d) + vd(1 - h) + v(1 - m) = 0$, he gives as a solution for v: $v = 0/[(1 - d) + d(1 - h) + (1 - m)]$. George Boole, *Collected Logical Works: The Laws of Thought* (LaSalle, Ill.: Open Court, 1952), II, 146.

40. Boole, II, p. 7; and see *W*, I, 223 (1865); *NEM*, IV, 117 (1909).

41. 3.440 (1896).

42. 3.47 (1870).

43. 3.182 (1880).

44. 3.446 (1896).

45. 2.356 (1895).

46. 3.175 (1867).

47. John S. Mill, *A System of Logic* (London: Longmans Green and Co., 1961), Book II; and see 4.76 (1893).

48. 3.184 (1880); and see 1.562 (1907).

49. Augustus DeMorgan, *On the Syllogism and Other Logical Writings*, ed. Peter Heath (New Haven: Yale University Press, 1966), p. 22; and see p. 51.

50. *NEM*, IV, 125 (1909); and see Charles S. Peirce, "The Century's Great Men in Science," *Charles S. Peirce Selected Writings*, ed. Philip P. Wiener (New York: Dover, 1966), p. 271.

51. *NEM*, III, 351 (1903), *NEM*, IV, 10 (1901).

52. *NEM*, IV, 11 (1901).

53. 2.323 (1902), 2.348 (1895), 4.48 (1893); *NEM*, II, 345 (1903), *NEM*, IV, 340 (1898).

54. 2.96 (1902).

55. 2.289 (1902), 2.339 (1895), 3.393 (1885).

56. 3.374 (1885).

57. Ibid.

58. 3.162 (1880), 3.154 (1880), 4.70–4.79 (1894), 4.86 (1894), 4.470 (1903), 5.367 (1877), 5.411 (1905).

59. 3.168 (1880); and see 2.462 (1867).

60. 7.536 (1899).

61. 4.94–4.106 (1893); *NEM*, III, 368 (1903), *NEM*, III, 466 (1899). *NEM*, III, 914 (1904).

62. *NEM*, IV, 315 (1906).

63. *NEM*, III, 792–3 (1897), *NEM*, IV, 314 (c. 1906).

64. *NEM*, III, 791 (1897).

65. *NEM*, III, 792 (1897).

66. 3.537 (1897), 5.178 (1903); and see Joseph W. Dauben, "C. S. Peirce's Philosophy of Infinite Sets," *Mathematical Magazine* 50, No. 3 (1977), 123, 135.

67. 5.425 (1905).

68. MS 458–29 (1903).

69. 4.114 (1894), 6.580 (1890), 6.585 (1890); *NEM*, IV, 127 (1897–98); MS 942 (1897–1898).

70. 3.315 (1880).

71. The x-axis is an asymptote iff the following: Let $x_0 = 0$. For any positive integer n there is a point x on the x-axis such that:

(1) $x_n > x_{n-1} + 1$
(2) the distance between x_n and the hyperbola is $< 1/n$;

and see *CD*, pp. 3458, 5025.
   72. MS 312–47 (1907); and see 5.146 (1903).
   73. See 5.411 (1905).
   74. 2.444 (1893), 3.472 (1897).

5. Critical Logic (2)

   1. MS 691–118 (1901); and see 6.531 (1901), 7.220 (1901).
   2. See above, pages 55, 58.
   3. 1.444 (1896).
   4. *NEM*, IV, 38 (1902).
   5. 5.579 (1898).
   6. 5.347–5.357 (1868); and see 2.690 (1883).
   7. 2.102 (1902).
   8. *NEM*, III, 214 (1910).
   9. 5.580 (1898).
  10. *NEM*, III, 757 (1893).
  11. 2.566 (1901); my italics.
  12. *NEM*, III, 180 (1911).
  13. *CD*, p. 3068 (1889).
  14. *NEM*, III, 178 (1911).
  15. *NEM*, III, 758 (1893).
  16. 2.642 (1878), 2.749 (1883); MSS 660–02 (1910), 766 (1897); and see Charles S. Peirce, "The Principles of Philosophy: Or, Logic, Physics and Psychics, Considered as a Unity in the Light of the Nineteenth Century" (Privately printed brochure) [P 00552]; *NEM*, III, 875 (1909).
  17. William Stanley Jevons, *The Principles of Science: A Treatise on Logic and Scientific Method* (London: Macmillan and Co., 1907), pp. 242–247.
  18. Jevons, p. 242.
  19. Jevons, p. 244.
  20. Charles S. Peirce, "On the Theory of Errors of Observation," *Report of the Superintendent of the U. S. Coast Survey* (Washington: Government Printing Office, 1870), 24th day, p. 224 [P 00077]; and see *NEM*, III, 639 (1870).
  21. *NEM*, III, 672 (1872).
  22. Jevons, pp. 224, 383.
  23. Jevons, p. 9.
  24. Jevons, pp. 134–137.
  25. *NEM*, III, 213 (1910).
  26. *NEM*, III, 173 (1911).
  27. 2.692 (1878): *NEM*, III, 875 (1909).
  28. *NEM*, III, 214 (1910).
  29. See 2.685 (1878).
  30. 2.703 (1883).
  31. 7.120 (1903), 7.209 (1903).
  32. 6.40 (1892).
  33. 2.776 (1902), 1.95 (1898), 2.789 (1902), 7.89 (1906).

34. Thomas A. Goudge, *The Thought of C. S. Peirce* (Toronto: University of Toronto Press, 1950), p. 162 [S 00565].

35. Chung-Ying Cheng, "Requirements for the Validity of Induction: An Examination of C. S. Peirce's Theory," *Philosophy and Phenomenological Research* 28 (1968), 392–402 [S 00257], and Chung-Ying Cheng, *Peirce's and Lewis's Theories of Induction* (The Hague: Martinus Nijhoff, 1969), p. 48 [S 00258].

36. 1.96 (1898); and see 2.738 (1883).

37. 2.696 (1883), 2.729 (1883).

38. 2.726 (1883).

39. 1.93 (1898).

40. Peirce refers to the central limit theorem at 2.758 (1908), 5.170 (1903), 6.100 (1902).

41. 2.269 (1902).

42. 2.703 (1883).

43. 2.102 (1902).

44. 2.763 (1908); and see Cheng's discussion in *Philosophy and Phenomenological Research* [S 00257].

45. 2.703 (1883).

46. 2.692 (1878), 7.110 (1903).

47. 7.207 (1903).

48. 2.693 (1878).

49. *NEM,* IV, 319 (1906); and see 2.269 (1903).

50. Alfred J. Ayer, *The Origins of Pragmatism: Studies in the Philosophy of Charles Sanders Peirce and William James* (San Francisco: Freeman, Cooper, 1968), p. 91 [S 00054]; Edward Madden, "Peirce on Probability," *Studies in the Philosophy of Charles Sanders Peirce,* Second Series, ed. Edward C. Moore and Richard S. Robin (Amherst: University of Massachusetts Press, 1964), p. 139 [S 00884]; Donald R. Koehn, "C. S. Peirce's 'Illustrations of the Logic of Science' and the Pragmatic Justification of Induction,"*Transactions* 9, No. 3 (1973) [S 00776].

51. Letter from C. S. P. to J. S. Mill, undated (1867?), Yale University Library Correspondence.

52. 2.744 (1883); *NEM,* III, 345 (1903); and see 2.96 (1902).

53. 2.96 (1902), 2.756 (1905), 2.759 (1905), 2.775 (1905), 5.170 (1903), 7.203 (1901), 7.114 (1903), 7.216 (1903); and see 2.269 (1903).

54. 2.756 (1905), 2.758 (1905), 7.113 (1903); and see 2.269 (1903).

55. 2.96 (1902).

56. Ibid.

57. Ibid.

58. 2.229 (1897); my italics.

59. 3.454 (1896).

6. Speculative Rhetoric (1)

1. 4.116 (1893), 8.342 (1908).

2. MS 595–24 (1895).

3. MSS 774–9 (1904), 449–26 (1903).

4. 2.229 (1897).

5. Aristotle, *Rhetoric,* 1329–26.

6. Ibid., 1354a–15.

7. *CD*, p. 1950; *W*, II, 24.

8. 2.106 (1902); MSS 449–24 (1903), 1334–30 (1905), 1334–50 (1905), 1338–44 (1905); in MS 1338–46 (1905), Peirce said the proper development of methodeutic must be based upon an accurate speculative grammar, by means of a scientifically exact intermediate doctrine of logical critic.

9. 2.96 (1902); and see MS 425A–156 (1902).

10. *NEM*, IV, xii; MS 1519 (undated).

11. 2.92 (1902).

12. 2.582 (1901); and see *NEM*, IV, 57 (1902). A leading principle is a proposition which we take to be true or approximately true and which expresses that a certain class of inferences are generally true. For example, the proposition, "If the kind of wire at hand is copper wire, then it will conduct electricity," is a leading principle (a material leading principle). The proposition, "If *All A is B and x is an A*, then *x is a B*," is another kind of leading principle (a formal leading principle). See 3.154–3.251 (1880).

13. 2.639 (1878), 5.591 (1903); MS 246–21 (1889).

14. MS 304–22 (1903); and see 1.316 (1903), 1.351 (1905), 7.679 (1903).

15. 3.527 (1897), 5.60 (1903), 8.244 (1905); MSS 426–12 (1902), 778–14 (1905), 1125 (1900), 1126 (1900).

16. Charles S. Peirce, "The English Doctrine of Ideas," review of *Analysis of the Phenomena of the Human Mind*, by James Mill; *The Nation* 9 (Nov. 1869), 461–462, rpt. in *N*, I, 32–37 [P 00045].

17. Ibid.

18. 5.382 note (1893).

19. 8.239 (1904), 3.566 (1900); MS 843 (1908).

20. 2.741–2.743 (1883); and see 6.98 (1902).

21. 7.201 (1901); and see 1.341 (1895), 1.422 (1896), 2.696 (1883), 2.776 (1902), 5.340 (1869).

22. MS 453–37 (1903).

23. 6.419 (1878), 7.208 (1901), 7.211 (1901).

24. *NEM*, IV, 19 (1902).

25. *NEM*, IV, 346 (1898).

26. Max H. Fisch, "Salomon Bochner on Charles S. Peirce," *American Mathematical Monthly* 82, No. 5 (May 1975), 481 [S 00489]; and see 6.173 (1902), 7.463 (1894), 7.565 (1893), 7.570 (1893); also see George Allen Benedict, "The Concept of Continuity in Charles Peirce's Synechism," diss. New York at Buffalo, 1973, p. 44 [S 00077]; Harbert William Davenport, "Peirce's Evolutionary Explanation of Laws of Nature: 1880–1893," diss. Illinois, 1977, p. 177 [S 00308].

27. 4.5 (1898), 6.568 (1890); and see 1.223 (1902), 3.454 (1896), 7.678 (1903); and James Feibleman, *An Introduction to the Philosophy of C. S. Peirce*, p. 346 [S 00451]. What Peirce called indagation resembled what F. E. Abbot called "the silent method of science."

28. 3.430 (1897), 3.454 (1896).

29. 6.102 (1892).

30. 6.25 (1891); and see *NEM*, IV, 378 (1892–3); MS 928 (1892–3).

31. 6.305 (1893).

32. 6.218 (1898).

33. *NEM*, IV, 378 (1 92–3); MS 928 (1892–3).

34. 5.317 (1868); anc see 1.316 (1903), 6.238 (1892), 7.585 (1866), [*Measure*

for Measure, II: 2, Isabella]. Peirce also writes, in MS L233 (1908): "My second article is intended to examine the most general hypotheses concerning the mind and soul. . . . I think I shall begin by describing what a row it created in philosophy when Lewes pointed out that consciousness must be regarded as an *epiphenomenon.* I shall show how we come by the notion of consciousness (in the sense in question). That we don't *observe* it. On the contrary, as Shakespeare says

Man, proud man
[is] Most ignorant of what he's most assured,
His glassy essence.

The notion is obtained by a process of prescission which I shall describe in some detail, and the resulting notion is therefore an abstract character."

7. Speculative Rhetoric (2)

1. 1.203 (1902).
2. 1.207 (1902), 2.646 (1878).
3. 2.646 (1878).
4. Ibid.
5. Ibid.
6. Max H. Fisch, "Peirce's Arisbe: The Greek Influence in His Later Philosophy," *Transactions* 7, No. 4 (Fall 1971) [S 00482].
7. 1.229 (1902); and see MSS 426–4 (1902), 427–45 to 48 (1902), 1344–11 (1902).
8. Louis Agassiz, *Essay on Classification,* ed. Edward Lurie (1857; rpt. Cambridge, Mass.: Belknap Press of Harvard University, 1962), p. 216.
9. Ibid., pp. 5, 139.
10. Ibid., p. 18.
11. Ibid., pp. 18, 19, 36, 46, 64, 98.
12. Ibid., p. 8.
13. Ibid., p. 9.
14. Ibid., p. 59.
15. Ibid., p. 157.
16. Ibid., p. 12.
17. Ibid., p. 9.
18. Charles S. Peirce, review of *Philosophy as Scientia Scientarium, and a History of Classifications of the Sciences,* by Robert Flint, *The Nation* 80 (May 1905), 360–361, rpt. in *N,* III,-215–218 [P 01091]; *NEM,* III, 1122 (1892); MS 1345 (1892); *NEM,* IV, 17 (1902).
19. 1.180–1.202 (1903); and see MS 675–10 (1911).
20. 1.222 (1902).
21. 1.223 (1902); and see *NEM,* IV, 64 (1902).
22. *NEM,* IV, 65 (1902).
23. 1.615 (1903); and see 1.44 (1898), 1.204 (1902), 1.230 (1902), 1.139 (1902); *NEM,* IV, xix (undated fragments); Letter from C. S. P. to James M. Peirce, October 25, 1895, in Max Fisch's Correspondence File; *CD,* p. 5396 (1898).

24. *NEM,* III, 867 (1909), *NEM,* IV, 29–31 (1902); 1.590 (1900); and see MS 392–5 (1873).

25. *NEM,* IV, 31 (1902); *W,* II, 339 (1869).

26. 6.6 (1906); MS 283-basis 11 (1906); and see 1.128 (1905), 1.620 (1898); MS 281–1 (1905).

27. *W,* II, 190 (1868).

28. 1.180 (1902); *NEM,* II, 10 (1895), *NEM,* II, 251 (1894), *NEM,* III, 366 (1903).

29. 1.226 (1902).

8. Speculative Rhetoric (3)

1. 6.10–6.12 (1891).

2. 1.250 (1902). At 1.351 C. S. P. says it is a fact that thought resembles nature. He does not always put it that strongly.

3. 7.381 (1902); and see MS 615–4 (1908), where Peirce says that one general agency, mind, animates alike the electron and the entire stellar system.

4. 5.388 (1878).

5. 5.402 (1878).

6. Charles S. Peirce, "Early Magnetical Science," review of *William Gilbert of Colchester,* trans. Fleury Mottelay, *The Nation* 58 (February 1894), 124–125, rpt. in *N,* II, 29 [P 00562]. Peirce says in a note that "The use of the word *manifestus* in this sense, which is almost peculiar to modern physicists, and that without explanation, seems to indicate the existence of a sufficiently large class of physicists early in the thirteenth century to have developed a diction of their own."

7. Henry Enfield Roscoe, *Spectrum Analysis* (New York: D. Appleton and Co., 1869), p. 242. These lectures were given in 1868 and there were four editions. Peirce reviewed the work in *The Nation* 9 (July 1869), 73–74, rpt. in *N,* I, 29 [P 00044].

8. MS 1047 (1861).

9. 1.394 (c. 1890), 6.242 (1892); and see *solid, CD,* p. 5758 (1889).

10. *CD,* p. 4371.

11. Ibid.

12. Charles S. Peirce, Letter, *The Nation* 77 (October 1903), 320, rpt. in *N,* III, 145–146 [P 01030].

13. Charles S. Peirce, "A Quincuncial Projection of the Sphere," *American Journal of Mathematics* 3 (1879), 394–396 [P 00135].

14. Benjamin Peirce, *Ideality in the Physical Sciences* (Boston: Little, Brown and Company, 1881), p. 28. And see C. S. P.'s own remarks on imaginaries and quaternions, to the effect that these reduce to matrices, mappings, or other *Abbildungen,* 4.132–4.133 (1893).

15. 6.72 (1898); and see *NEM,* III, 150 (1909).

16. 7.471 (1898).

17. *NEM,* III, 154 (1909).

18. 6.299 (1893); MS 427–34 (1902); Peirce observed, also, that the state descriptions for states of conservative systems were expressed in terms of virtual displacements, virtual velocities, and virtual work, and this lent itself to expression in the illative form; 6.68 (1898); MSS 641–33 (1909), 662 (1901),

916A–77 (1861), 1041 (1905). Also see Charles S. Peirce, "Note on the Effect of the Flexure of a Pendulum upon its Period of Oscillation," *Report of the Superintendent of the U. S. Coast and Geodetic Survey* (Washington: Government Printing Office, 1884), pp. 483–485, where Peirce objects to the term *potential energy*. In 8.318 (1891) Peirce says the law of mind *forbids* the reversal of physical processes.

19. 6.24 (1891), 6.72 (1898), 6.85 (1898), MS 956 (1890).
20. 6.79–6.80 (1898), MS 717 (1895) [moved from MS 950 (1893)].
21. 6.79 (1898).
22. *NEM*, IV, xvi (undated fragment).
23. 1.393 (c. 1890), 6.246 (1892).
24. *NEM*, III, 892 (1908).
25. 7.43 (1907).
26. The entry "Atoms, molecules, vortices" in Fisch's *Subject File*, marked "5b folded sheet of Parson's Paper Company"; and see 4.611 (1908), 4.648 (1907), MS 4–45 (1904).
27. 8.274 (1902); and see 1.276 (1902), 4.611 note (1908); *NEM*, III, 898 (1908). At 1.276 Peirce uses a similar spiral function:

$$1/\{r - (1/2 \text{ inch})\} = 3 \log \{1 + \text{antilog} (90°/\theta - 90°)\}$$

to represent not the mind-body system but a universe of a certain kind. In this case the spiral pauses in the neighborhood of 1.6 and, though Peirce says it abruptly stops at r = 3 1/2, the curve continues on to the right indefinitely (see graph).

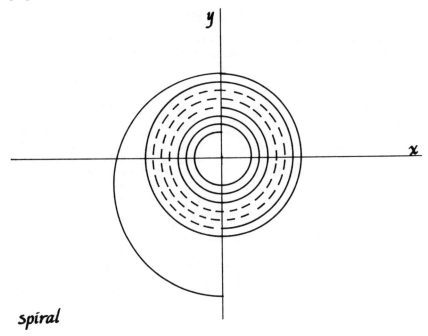

spiral

28. F. A. Kekule, "The Scientific Aims and Achievements of Chemistry," *Nature* XVIII (June 20, 1878), 210–213. (All of the italics are Kekule's except the sentence, "But . . . investigation.")

29. MS 1317–6 (c.1890).

30. 1.220 (1902); and see MS 246–10 (1889). In the *Century Dictionary and Cyclopedia*, 10 vols. (New York: The Century Company, 1899), VIII, 6789 [P 00373] Peirce describes the vortex atoms as

> A whirl of fluid. An intuitive geometrical idea of the motion is not easily attained. If the motion of a fluid varies continuously both in time and in space, it may be described as such that each spherical particle is at each instant receiving three compressions or elongations at right angles to one another, and has, besides, a motion of translation and a motion of rotation about an axis through it. When this motion of rotation is present, the fluid is said to have a rotational motion; but this must not be confounded with a rotation of the whole mass. Thus, if all the parts of the fluid move in one direction but with unequal velocities in different parallel planes, though there be no rotation of the whole mass, yet the motion is rotational; and if a spherical particle were suddenly congealed, its inertia would make it rotate. On the other hand, one or more radial paddles turning about the axis of a cylindrical vessel filled with a perfect fluid, though making the latter revolve as a whole, could yet impart no rotational motion, which the fluid would evade by slipping round between the paddles. The motion being perfectly continuous, the axis of rotation of a particle must join the axis of rotation of a neighboring particle, so that a curve, called a *vortex-line,* may be described whose tangents are the axes of rotation of the particles at their points of tangency; and such a curve must evidently return into itself or reach both extremities to the boundaries of the fluid. A vortex is a portion of fluid in rotational motion inclosed in an annular surface which is a locus of vortex-lines; and an infinitesimal vortex is called a *vortex-filament.* If at any part of a vortex-filament the angular velocity is greater than at another part a little removed along the vortex-line, then (considering a particle a little removed from the central vortex-line) it is plain that of two opposite parts of this particle having the same velocity in magnitude and direction and consequently on its axis of rotation, that one which is in the more rapidly moving stratum must be nearer the central vortex-line, so that the annular boundary of the vortex must present a constriction where the angular velocity is great; and thus it can be shown that the product of the mean angular velocity in any cross-section perpendicular to the vortex-lines multiplied by the area of that section is constant at all parts of the vortex. In a perfect fluid, which can sustain no distorting stress even for an instant, the velocity of a rotating particle cannot be retarded any more than if it were a frictionless sphere; and, in like manner, no such velocity can be increased. Consequently, a vortex, unlike a wave, continues to be composed of the same identical matter. When the motion is continuous throughout the fluid, two vortices exercise a singular action upon one another, each ring in turn contracting and passing through the apertures of the other, which stretches, with other singular motions.

Peirce thought the best way to arrange the ideas of topology was, like all other ideas, by *connective valency.* This is relevant to his conception of the vortex atom, because it issues in the theory of knots. *NEM,* II, 274, 281, 289 ff., 308 (and MS 94 [1894]).

31. The entry "Atoms, molecules, vortices" in Max Fisch's *Subject File,* marked "5b folded sheet of Parson's Paper Company"; and see 1.249 (1902); MSS 283–26 (1906), 938–6 (1904).

32. 4.309 (1902); and see MS 643–44 (1909).

33. 4.309 (1902).

34. *W,* I, 95 (1863).

35. *W,* II, 344 (1869).

36. See Fisch's *Subject File,* "Argon, Helium and Helium's Partner," [IClb 11(a)]; and see 1.403 (c. 1890), 2.636 (1878), 5.586 (1898); MSS 660–09 (1910), 693b–122 (1904).

37. 6.242 (1892).

38. 6.243 (1892).

39. MS 290–39 (1905).

40. MS 427A–146 (1902).

41. Charles S. Peirce, review of *Molecules and the Molecular Theory of Matter,* by A. D. Risteen, *The Nation* 62 (February, 1896), 147, rpt. in *N,* II, 129 [P 00625]; and see 6.243 (1892).

42. 6.242–6.244 (1892).

43. *NEM,* III, 915 (1904).

44. 1.422 (1896).

45. *NEM,* III, 351 (1903).

46. *NEM,* III, 758 (1893).

47. 2.339 (1902).

48. 1.434 (1896), 5.448 (1905), 6.232 (1898).

49. *NEM,* II, 528 (1904), *NEM,* III, 867 (1909).

50. 6.219 (1898).

51. 1.488 (1896), 6.232 (1898); *NEM,* III, 59 (1895), *NEM,* III, 340 (1903), *NEM,* III, 891 (1908).

52. 1.430 (1896).

BIBLIOGRAPHY

Agassiz, Louis. *Essay on Classification*. Ed. Edward Lurie. 1867: rpt. Cambridge, Mass.: The Belknap Press of Harvard University, 1962.

Anderson, Paul, and Max Fisch. *Philosophy in America*. New York: Appleton-Century-Crofts, Inc., 1939.

Apel, Karl-Otto. *Charles S. Peirce from Pragmatism to Pragmaticism*. Trans. John Michael Krois. Amherst: University of Massachusetts Press, 1981.

Aristotle's Metaphysics. Tr. W. D. Ross. 2 vols. Oxford: Oxford University Press.

Ayer, Alfred J. *The Origins of Pragmatism: Studies in the Philosophy of Charles Peirce and William James*. San Francisco: Freeman, Cooper, 1968.

Berry, Arthur. *A Short History of Astronomy*. New York: Dover, 1961.

Black, Max. "Vagueness." *Philosophy of Science* 4 (1937), 427–455.

Boole, George. *Collected Logical Works: The Laws of Thought*. LaSalle, Ill.: Open Court, 1952.

Brunning, J. "Peirce's Development of the Algebra of Relations." Diss., University of Toronto, 1981.

Buchler, Justus. "The Accidents of Peirce's System." *Journal of Philosophy* 37 (1940): 364–369.

Burks, Arthur W., ed. *Collected Papers of Charles Sanders Peirce*. Vols. VII and VIII. Cambridge, Mass.: The Belknap Press of Harvard University, 1966.

Butterfield, H. *The Origins of Modern Science*. London: Bell, 1949.

Carnap, Rudolf. *Logical Foundations of Probability*. Chicago: 1950.

Cheng, Chung-Ying. *Peirce's and Lewis's Theories of Induction*. The Hague: Martinus Nijhoff, 1969.

———. "Requirements for the Validity of Induction: An Examination of C. S. Peirce's Theory." *Philosophy and Phenomenological Research* 28 (1968).

Cohen, Morris, ed. *Chance, Love and Logic*. New York: Barnes and Noble, Inc., 1923.

Cook, James Edward, and Kenneth Laine Ketner. *Charles Sanders Peirce: Contributions to The Nation*, Part I (1869–1893), Part II (1894–1900), Part III (1901–1908). Lubbock, Texas: Texas Tech Press, 1975, 1978, 1979.

Deely, John. *Introducing Semiotic, Its History and Doctrine*. Bloomington: Indiana University Press, 1982.

DeMorgan, Augustus. *On the Syllogism and Other Logical Writings*. 1850; rpt. New Haven: Yale University Press, 1966.

Eisele, Carolyn, ed. *The New Elements of Mathematics by Charles S. Peirce*. 4 vols. (in 5). The Hague: Mouton, 1976.

———. "Modern Mathematical Exactitude in Peirce's 'Doctrine of Exact Philosophy.' " *Proceedings of CSP Bicentennial International Congress*. Lubbock, Texas: Texas Tech Press, 1981.

———. "Mathematical Methodology in the Thought of Charles S. Peirce." *Historia Mathematica* 9, No. 3 (1982), 333–341.

Esposito, Joseph. *Evolutionary Metaphysics: The Development of Peirce's Theory of Categories*. Athens, Ohio: Ohio University Press, 1980.

Feibleman, James K. *An Introduction to the Philosophy of Charles S. Peirce Interpreted as a System*. Cambridge, Mass.: M.I.T. Press, 1970.

Fisch, Max H., et al., eds. *Writings of Charles S. Peirce: A Chronological Edition*. Vols I and II. Bloomington: Indiana University Press, 1982.

———. "Just *How* General is Peirce's General Theory of Signs?" *American Journal of Semiotics* 2, Nos. 1–2 (1983), 55–60.

———. "Salomon Bochner on Charles S. Peirce." *American Mathematical Monthly* 82, No. 5 (May 1975), 478–481.

Fraser, D. A. S. *Statistics, An Introduction*. New York: John Wiley and Sons, Inc., 1958.

Gingerich, Owen, ed. *The Nature of Scientific Discovery*. Washington: Smithsonian Institution Press, 1975.

Goudge, Thomas A. *The Thought of C. S. Peirce*. Toronto: University of Toronto Press, 1950.

Greenlee, Douglas. *Peirce's Concept of Sign*. The Hague: Mouton, 1973.

Hanson, Norwood. *Patterns of Discovery*. Cambridge: Cambridge University Press, 1965.

Hartshorne, Charles, and Paul Weiss, eds. *Collected Papers of Charles Sanders Peirce*. Vols. I–VI. Cambridge, Mass.: The Belknap Press of Harvard University, 1965.

Herzberger, H. *Pragmatism and Purpose: Essays Presented to Thomas A. Goudge*. Ed. J. G. Slater, T. Wilson, and T. W. Summer. Toronto: University of Toronto Press, 1981.

Huggett, John W. "Charles Peirce's Search for a Method." Diss., University of Toronto, 1954.

Hume, David. *An Enquiry Concerning Human Understanding*. New York: The Liberal Arts Press, 1955.

Jevons, William S. *The Principles of Science: A Treatise on Logic and Scientific Method*. London: Macmillan and Co., 1907.

Kekule, F. A. "The Scientific Aims and Achievements of Chemistry." *Nature*, June 20, 1878; vol. 18, 210–213.

Kepler, Johannes. *The Secret of the Universe*. Trans. A. M. Duncan. New York: John Wiley and Sons, Inc., 1958.

Ketner, Kenneth Laine. "Carolyn Eisele's Place in Peirce Studies." *Historia Mathematica* 9, No. 3 (1982), 326–332.

———. "A Brief Intellectual Autobiography by Charles Sanders Peirce." *American Journal of Semiotics* 2, Nos. 1–2 (1983), 61–83.

Ketner, Kenneth Laine, et al., eds. *A Comprehensive Bibliography and Index of the Published Works of Charles Sanders Peirce with a Bibliography of Secondary Studies*. Greenwich, Conn.: Johnson Associates, Inc., 1977.

Ketner, Kenneth Laine, and James Edward Cook, eds. *Charles Sanders Peirce: Contributions to the Nation*. Part One: 1869–1893, Part two: 1894–1900, Part three: 1901–1908. Lubbock: Texas Tech Press, 1975, 1978, 1979.

Kneale, William. *Probability and Induction*. Oxford: Clarendon Press, 1963.

Kuhn, Thomas. *The Structure of Scientific Revolution*. Chicago: University of Chicago Press, 1962.

Laplace, Pierre. *Celestial Mechanics*. Trans. Nathaniel Bowditch (1829, 1832, 1834, 1839). Bronx, N. Y.: Chelsea Publishing Co., Inc., 1966.

Lenzen, Victor. *Benjamin Peirce and the U. S. Coast Survey.* San Francisco: San Francisco Press, Inc., 1968.

Lieb, Irwin C. "New Studies in the Philosophy of Charles S. Peirce." *Review of Metaphysics* 8 (1954), 291–320.

Mill, John S. *A System of Logic.* London: Longmans Green and Co., Ltd., 1961.

Moore, Edward C., and Richard S. Robin. *Studies in the Philosophy of Charles Sanders Peirce, Second Series.* Amherst: University of Massachusetts Press, 1964.

Mora, José F. "Peirce's Conception of Architectonic and Related Views." *Philosophy and Phenomenological (Research) Thought,* 1955; 351–359.

Murphey, Murray G. *The Development of Peirce's Philosophy.* Cambridge, Mass.: Harvard University Press, 1961.

Newman, James R., ed. *The World of Mathematics.* Vols. I and II. New York: Simon and Schuster, 1956.

Nickles, Thomas, ed. *Scientific Discovery, Logic and Rationality;* and *Scientific Discovery: Case Studies.* Vols. LVI and LX in *Boston Studies in the Philosophy of Science.* Dordrecht, Holland: D. Reidel, 1980.

Peirce, Benjamin. *Analytic Mechanics.* Boston: Little, Brown and Co., 1885.

———. *Ideality in the Physical Sciences.* Boston: Little, Brown and Co., 1881.

Peirce, Charles S. *Photometric Researches.* Vol. IX in *Annals of the Harvard College Observatory.* Leipzig, 1878.

Putnam, Hilary. "Peirce the Logician." *Historia Mathematica* 9, No. 3 (1982): 290–301.

Quine, W. V., and J. S. Ullian. *The Web of Belief.* New York: Random House, 1970.

Reichenbach, Hans. *The Theory of Probability.* Trans. E. H. Hutten and M. Reichenbach. Berkeley, Cal.: University of California Press, 1949.

Report of the Superintendent of the U. S. Coast and Geodetic Survey. Government Printing Office, 1870, 1881, 1884.

Rescher, Nicholas. *Peirce's Philosophy of Science: Critical Studies in His Theory of Induction and Scientific Method.* Notre Dame, Indiana: University of Notre Dame Press, 1978.

Robin, Richard S., ed. *Annotated Catalogue of the Papers of Charles S. Peirce.* Amherst, Mass.: The University of Massachusetts Press, 1967.

Roscoe, Henry Enfield. *Spectrum Analysis.* New York: D. Appleton and Co., 1869.

Rowland, H. A. "Concave Gratings for Optical Purposes." *The American Journal of Science* XXVI (1883).

Royce, Josiah. *Basic Writings of Josiah Royce.* Ed. John J. Mcdermott. Chicago: University of Chicago Press, 1969.

Schröder, E. *Vorlesungen über die Algebra der Logik (Exakte Logik).* Leipzig: B. G. Teubner, 1980.

Stevens, Peter S. *Patterns in Nature.* New York: Penguin Books, 1977.

Tait, Peter Guthrie, and Sir William Thomson. *Elements of Natural Philosophy.* Cambridge: Cambridge University Press, 1912.

Transactions of the Charles S. Peirce Society: A Quarterly Journal in American Philosophy. Vols. I–XXI (1965–1985).

von Wright, G. H. *The Logical Problem of Induction.* New York: Macmillan Co., 1957.

Weiss, Paul. "The Essence of Peirce's System." *Journal of Philosophy* 37 (1940), 353–364.

Weyl, H. *Philosophy of Mathematics and Natural Science.* Princeton: Princeton University Press, 1949. Originally published in *Handbuch der Philosophie: Philosophie der Mathematik und Naturwissenschaft.* R. Oldenbourg, 1927.

Whewell, William. *The History of the Inductive Sciences.* 3 vols. London: Cass, 1967, *The Philosophy of the Inductive Sciences.* 2 vols. London: Cass, 1967.

Whitney, William D., et al., eds. *The Century Dictionary and Cyclopedia.* 8 vols. New York: The Century Co., 1889.

Wiener, Philip P. *Charles S. Peirce: Selected Writings.* New York: Dover, 1966.

Young, Frederick H., and Philip Wiener. *Studies in the Philosophy of Charles Sanders Peirce.* Cambridge, Mass.: Harvard University Press, 1952.

Zöllner, Johann C. F. *Photometrische Untersuchungen.* Leipzig: Wilhelm Engelmann, 1865.

INDEX

RICHARD TURSMAN, Associate Professor of Philosophy at Glendon College, York University, in Toronto, is a contributing editor to *Writings of Charles S. Peirce: A Chronological Edition.*